ENGLISH FOR INTERNATIONAL COMMUNICATION

For Beginners

New Edition

英語數位學習第一品牌

ENGLISH FOR INTERNATIONAL COMMUNICATION
For Beginners
New Edition

發 行 人	鄭俊琪
總 編 輯	陳豫弘
副總編輯	璩雅琪
中文編輯	莊琬茹、林怡君、楊貽惠、張珮絹
英文編輯	Courtney Aldrich、Lara Cooper、Michael Coughlin
英文錄音	James Baron、Tom Brink、Stephanie Buckley、Jerome Villegas、Courtney Aldrich、Doug Nienhuis、Helen Yeh、Jenny Wilsen、Michael Coughlin、Meagunn Hart、David Rowswell、Nicholas Wheeler
藝術總監	李尚竹
美術編輯	林士琪、周秀圓
技術總監	李志純
介面設計	李海瑄
程式設計	李志純、郭曉琪
光碟製作	姜尹涵
出版發行	希伯崙股份有限公司 105 台北市松山區八德路 3 段 32 號 12 樓 劃撥：1939-5400 電話：(02) 2578-7838 傳真：(02) 2578-5800 電子郵件：Service@LiveABC.com
法律顧問	朋博法律事務所
印　　刷	禹利電子分色有限公司
出版日期	2014 年 5 月 初版一刷 2016 年 8 月 初版五刷 2018 年 2 月 再版一刷

出版品預行編目 (CIP) 資料

English for international communication for beginners / 陳豫弘總編輯．
—— 再版．—— 臺北市：希伯崙公司，2018.02
面； 公分
ISBN 978-986-441-206-8(平裝)
1. 多益測驗
805.1895　　　　　　　　　　107000124

本書若有缺頁、破損、裝訂錯誤，請寄回本公司更換
版權所有，禁止以任何方式，在任何地方作全部或局部翻印、仿製或轉載
© 2018 by LiveABC Interactive Corporation
All rights reserved. Printed in Taiwan

English For International Communication

For Beginners

New Edition

目錄　Table of Contents

編輯室報告 ……………………………………………………………… 6
應考資訊 ………………………………………………………………… 8
光碟使用說明 …………………………………………………………… 12

Part 1　Photographs 照片描述

- 題型介紹 & 基本作答技巧　13
- 四大類照片題範例與解題技巧　14
- 八大照片題之場景與搶分詞彙　18
- Practice Test　26

Part 2　Question and Response 應答問題

- 題型介紹 & 基本作答技巧　29
- 題型分析圖　30
- 題型 1：Wh- Questions　32
- 題型 2：Yes/No Questions　38
- 題型 3：A or B Questions　42
- 題型 4：Statements　43
- Practice Test　44

Part 3　Short Conversations 簡短對話

- 題型介紹 & 基本作答流程與技巧　45
- Part 3 應考概念與技巧　46
- 題型 1：與「人物」有關　48
- 題型 2：與「事件」有關　50
- 題型 3：與「細節」有關　52
- 題型 4：推論題　54
- 題型 5：考口語用法或句意　56
- 題型 6：圖表題　58
- Practice Test　60

Part 4　Short Talks 簡短獨白

- 題型介紹 & 基本作答流程與技巧　67
- 常考題型　68
- 獨白類型與常考問題　70
- 獨白類型 1：Announcement 公告或宣布　72
- 獨白類型 2：Introduction 介紹或引言　74
- 獨白類型 3：Media Broadcast 廣播或電視媒體　76

		• 獨白類型 4：Voice Message 語音訊息	78
		• 獨白類型 5：Speech/Lecture 演講	80
		📝 Practice Test	82
Part 5	Incomplete Sentences 句子填空	• 題型介紹 & 基本作答流程與技巧	87
		• 解題步驟與題型分析	88
		• 題型 1：詞性題	90
		• 題型 2：時態題	92
		• 題型 3：單字片語題	94
		• 題型 4：文法題	96
		📝 Practice Test	108
Part 6	Text Completion 段落填空	• 題型介紹 & 基本作答技巧	113
		• 題目範例與解析	114
		• 多益必備詞彙	116
		📝 Practice Test	118
Part 7	Reading Comprehension 閱讀測驗	• 題型介紹 & 基本作答流程與技巧	121
		• 常考題型與解題技巧	122
		• 文章類型與閱讀重點	123
		• 常考文章類型與考題範例：廣告	124
		• 常考文章類型與考題範例：書信	126
		• 常考文章類型與考題範例：即時訊息對話	128
		• 常考文章類型與考題範例：雙篇文章	130
		• 常考文章類型與考題範例：多篇文章	132
		📝 Practice Test	135

New TOEIC Model Test 多益全真模擬試題 ……………………… 161

編輯室報告 From the Editor

根據美國教育測驗服務社（Educational Testing Service, ETS）台灣區代表的官方統計，近幾年台灣多益測驗考生的平均成績大多落在 530~550 分之間，而多益成績 550 分亦是許多企業徵選人才時的基本門檻。對於初次準備應考多益測驗的考生來說，往往希望能在忙碌的課業或工作之餘，在短時間內迅速達到理想的多益成績。本書以最精簡及系統化的方式統整歸納多益測驗各大題型，並輔以易於消化吸收且一目了然的圖表與表格，幫助讀者迅速掌握多益常考題型及應考技巧。

本書基本架構與特色如下：

1. 以表格呈現多益各大題型考法與基本作答技巧

▲ 每單元一開始先歸納多益各大題的題數、考法、題目時間間隔或建議作答時間，並提供考題範例及基本作答流程與技巧，讓讀者迅速掌握應考方式與應答訣竅。

2. 統整歸納題型與解題技巧，並提供範例與練習

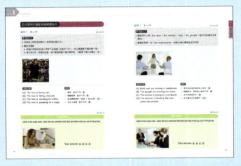 

▲ 例如 Part 1「照片描述」中多人照的解題技巧是要觀察其中人物動作的共通性及差異性；物件照則要留意擺放位置及相對關係等。Part 5「句子填空」則將考題歸納為詞性、時態、單字片語與文法等四大題型，各類題型皆提供重點整理與練習題。

3. 以圖表及系統化的分析破解多益常考題型

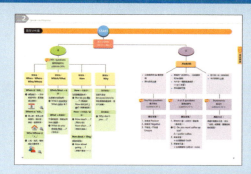
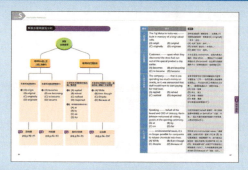

▲ 以圖表分析解題步驟與常考題型，使考生答題思路更清晰、輕鬆應付各類考題。

4. 整理常考字彙與搭配詞組，由專業外師錄音示範正確發音

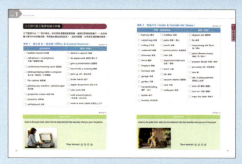

▲ 條列 Part 1「照片描述」中常見場景的重要詞彙，以及 Part 5「句子填空」及 Part 6「段落填空」的常考詞組與慣用語等，有助於考生增加字彙與應考實力，亦能強化在國際英語環境中的溝通能力。

5. 附完整多益模擬試題

▲ 仿照多益測驗命題的全真模擬測驗，讓讀者做完整 200 題的測驗，練習考試速度的掌控並測試學習成效。

相信讀者藉由本書有系統、有條理的題型分析與指引，加上不斷練習各類常考問題（全書超過 400 道練習與測驗題），必能迅速有效地戰勝多益測驗並增進職場競爭力。

Live ABC 編輯部 謹致

應考資訊 Test Information

一、什麼是多益測驗？

TOEIC 多益測驗全名是 Test of English for International Communication（國際溝通英語測驗），這是針對英語非母語人士所設計之英語能力測驗，其測驗分數反映受測者在國際職場環境中與他人以英語溝通的熟稔程度。

二、誰需要多益認證？

每天工作環境中會用到英語之人士，例如在企業、飯店、醫院、餐廳、航空業、以及經常要出席國際會議的專業人士。

- 跨國企業的員工，英語已經成為必要的工具。
- 欲在履歷表與學歷證件上，附有經國際肯定的英語能力檢定者。

跨國企業以及其他民營機構皆可以採用多益測驗來因應下列的需要：

- 招募員工時可設定應徵或報名考試之標準。
- 評量員工英語程度作為升等、海外受訓及開會的甄選參考。
- 作為英語進修課程編班標準以及檢定進修效果。

三、多益測驗方式為何？

- 分兩大類（two categories）：聽力（Listening）及閱讀（Reading）。
- 總題數：每部分各一百題，總共二百題。
- 測驗時間：聽力部分約四十五分鐘，閱讀部分七十五分鐘，總共兩小時。
- 類型：全部為 單選題 。考生選好答案後，要在與題目卷分開的答案卷上畫卡。

第一大類： 聽力

共四部分（4 parts）。考生會聽到各種主題英語的直述句、問句、對話以及獨白，然後根據所聽到的內容回答問題。

大題	題型	題數	新制題型變更細節
Part 1	照片描述（Photographs）	6 題（四選一）	
Part 2	應答問題（Question-Response）	25 題（三選一）	
Part 3	對話（Conversations）	13 組對話共 39 題（四選一）	・新增三人對話 ・融合圖表 ・考口語說法或句意
Part 4	獨白（Talks）	10 組獨白共 30 題（四選一）	・融合圖表 ・考口語說法或句意

第二大類： 閱讀

共三部分（3 parts）。題目及選項都印在題本上。考生須閱讀多種題材的文章，然後回答相關問題。你可以自由調配閱讀及答題速度。

大題	題型	題數	新制題型變更細節
Part 5	句子填空（Incomplete Sentences）	30 題（四選一）	
Part 6	段落填空（Text Completion）	16 題（四選一）	・加入句子插入題型，測驗考生是否理解文章上下文意及脈絡。
Part 7	閱讀測驗（Reading Comprehension） ● 單篇閱讀（Single Passages） ● 多篇閱讀（Multiple Passages） 　・雙篇閱讀（Double Passages） 　・三篇閱讀（Triple Passages）	● 單篇共 10 篇文章共 29 題（四選一） ● 多篇 5 組文章共 25 題（四選一）	・新增文字簡訊、即時通訊或多人互動的線上聊天訊息內容。 ・加入引述文章部分內容，測驗考生是否理解作者希望表達的意思。 ・除原有雙篇閱讀題組之外，新增三篇閱讀題組。

在正式考試前，會有大約三十分鐘填寫個人資料和問卷的時間，因此真正待在考場內時間大約為二小時三十分，中間不休息。

四、多益測驗考哪些內容？

多益測驗的設計以職場需要為主。測驗題的內容是從全世界各地職場的英文資料中蒐集而來，題材多元，包含各種地點與狀況，依字母排列分類如下：

企業發展 Corporate Development	● 研究（research） ● 產品研發（product development）
外食 Dining Out	● 商務／非正式午餐（business & informal lunches） ● 宴會（banquets） ● 招待會（receptions） ● 餐廳訂位（restaurant reservations）
娛樂 Entertainment	● 電影（cinema / movies） ● 劇場（theater）　　● 音樂（music） ● 藝術（art）　　　　● 展覽（exhibitions） ● 博物館（museums）　● 媒體（media）
金融／預算 Finance & Budgeting	● 銀行業務（banking）　● 投資（investments） ● 稅務（taxes）　　　　● 會計（accounting） ● 帳單（billing）
一般商務 General Business	● 契約（contracts）　　● 談判（negotiations） ● 企業合併（mergers）　● 行銷（marketing） ● 銷售（sales）　　　　● 保固（warranties） ● 商業企劃（business planning） ● 會議（conferences） ● 雇主員工關係（labor relations）

應考資訊 Test Information

保健 Health	• 醫藥保險（medical insurance） • 看醫生或牙醫（visiting doctors or dentists） • 去診所或醫院（going to the clinic or the hospital）
房屋／公司地產 Housing / Corporate Property	• 建築（construction） • 規格（specifications） • 購買和租賃（buying and renting） • 電力瓦斯服務（electric and gas services）
製造業 Manufacturing	• 工廠管理（plant management） • 生產線（assembly lines） • 品管（quality control）
辦公室 Offices	• 董事會（board meetings） • 委員會（committees） • 信件（letters） • 備忘錄（memoranda） • 電話留言、傳真訊息及電子郵件 （telephone, fax, and e-mail messages） • 辦公室設備和器材（office equipment & furniture） • 辦公室流程（office procedures）
人事 Personnel	• 招考（recruiting）　• 雇用（hiring） • 退休（retiring）　• 薪資（salaries） • 升遷（promotions）• 退休金（pensions） • 獎勵（awards） • 求職申請表（job applications） • 徵才廣告（job advertisements）
採購 Purchasing	• 採買（shopping）　• 訂貨（ordering supplies） • 送貨（shipping）　• 發票（invoices）
技術層面 Technical Areas	• 電子（electronics）• 科技（technology） • 電腦（computers） • 實驗室與相關器材（laboratories & related equipment） • 技術規格（technical specifications）
旅遊 Travel	• 火車（trains）　　• 飛機（airplanes） • 計程車（taxis）　• 巴士（buses） • 船隻（ships）　　• 渡輪（ferries） • 票務（tickets）　• 時刻表（schedules） • 車站和機場廣播（station & airport announcements） • 租車（car rentals） • 飯店（hotels） • 預訂（reservations） • 脫班與取消（delays and cancellations）

雖然取材自這麼多領域，但考生不需要具備各個領域之專業辭彙，而是以整體一般用字遣詞之熟悉與了解為主。

五、TOEIC 成績與英語能力參照

多益測驗的計分方式由答對題數決定,再將每一大類(聽力類、閱讀類)答對題數轉換成分數,總分在 10 分到 990 分之間。得到不同的成績代表擁有不同層級的英語能力,請參閱以下對照表。

TOEIC 成績	語言能力	證書顏色
905–990	英語能力已十分接近英語母語人士,能夠流暢有條理的表達意見、參與談話、主持英文會議、調和衝突並做出結論,語言使用上即使有瑕疵,亦不會造成理解上的困擾。	金色 (860–990)
785–900	可有效運用英語滿足社交及工作所需,措詞恰當,表達流暢;但在某些特定情形下,如:面臨緊張壓力、討論話題過於冷僻艱澀時,仍會顯現出語言能力不足的狀況。	藍色 (730–855)
605–780	可以英語進行一般社交場合的談話,能夠應付例行性的業務需求、參加英文會議、聽取大部分要點;但無法流利的以英語發表意見、作辯論,使用的字彙、句型亦以一般常見者為主。	綠色 (470–725)
405–600	英文文字溝通能力尚可,會話方面稍嫌辭彙不足、語言簡單,但已能掌握少量工作相關語言,可以從事英語相關程度較低的工作。	
255–400	語言能力僅僅侷限在簡單的一般日常對話,同時無法做連續性交談,亦無法用英文工作。	棕色 (220–465)
10–250	只能以背誦的句子進行問答而不能自行造句,尚無法將英語當作溝通工具來使用。	橘色 (10–215)

六、答題時間分配表

多益測驗須在 120 分鐘之內做完 200 道題目,考驗著應試者的耐力及應試技巧與策略。以下表列各個大題之題目難易度與考試時間分配策略,在閱讀測驗中尤其要注意作答時間的掌控。初次應考以 550 分為目標的考生,務必先掌握「低、中階」難度的題型,確定能達到以下目標答題率及答對題數後,再循序漸進攻占難度較高的題型。

	總題數	相對難易度	目標答對題數	目標答題率	目標得分	時間分配
聽力 Listening	100		53	53%		45 分鐘
Part 1	6	低	5	80%		
Part 2	25	低/中	18	72%	275	隨錄音播放速度
Part 3	39	中/高	20	50%		
Part 4	30	中/高	10	33%		
閱讀 Reading	100		63	63%		75 分鐘
Part 5	30	低/中	18	62%		12 分鐘
Part 6	16	低/中	11	67%	275	8 分鐘
Part 7	54	低/中/高	34	63%		55 分鐘
Total	200		116	58%	550	120 分鐘

User Guide 光碟使用說明

光碟安裝程序

步驟一 進入中文視窗。

步驟二 將光碟片放進光碟機。

步驟三 本產品備有 Auto Run 執行功能，如果您的電腦支援 Auto Run 光碟程式自動執行規格，則將自動顯現本書安裝畫面。

如果您的電腦已安裝過本公司產品，如【CNN 互動英語雜誌】或【Live 互動英語雜誌】等，您可以直接點選「快速安裝」圖示，進行快速安裝；否則，請點選「安裝」圖示，進行安裝。

操作說明

點選「執行」，即進入本光碟的教學課程。書中各單元內容以電子書方式呈現，整合文字、音檔及答題反應功能。主要操作方式說明如下：

◉ 主畫面

說明：

1. 主畫面有 8 個圖示，分別為本書 7 個單元以及「多益全真模擬試題」之按鍵名稱。畫面下方另有「操作說明」、「LiveABC 網站」以及「離開」的功能鍵。
2. 點選各單元按鍵即進入學習或測驗畫面。

◉ 單元學習畫面

- 點選 ▶PLAY 圖示即可聆聽音檔。
- 滾動滑鼠即可上下移動該頁面。
- 主要常考詞彙或示範例句亦可單獨點選聆聽發音。
- 練習題作答後立即知道答案是否正確。

📋 點選可查看目錄，並可在此選擇想學習的其他單元。

- Part 1: Photographs 照片描述
- Part 2: Question and Response 應答問題
- Part 3: Short Conversations 簡短對話
- Part 4: Short Talks 簡短獨白
- Part 5: Incomplete Sentences 句子填空
- Part 6: Text Completion 段落填空
- Part 7: Reading Comprehension 閱讀測驗

⬆單元 ⬇單元 點選可連結至上一單元／下一單元。

⬆頁 ⬇頁 點選可連結至該單元之上一頁／下一頁。

🏠主畫面 點選可回到主畫面。

◉ 模擬測驗畫面

- 附完整多益模擬測驗練習，作答完畢後電腦自動統計成績。

操作說明

在主畫面點選「操作說明」圖示，提供光碟操作說明。

LiveABC 網站

點選本圖示，將連結到 LiveABC 英文學習網站，您可以在網站上獲得更多最新消息。

內文朗讀 MP3

光碟中含全書 MP3 內容，您可以將光碟置於電腦中，從「我的電腦」點選您的光碟機，再從中選擇光碟資料夾裡的 MP3 檔案夾，使用播放器軟體將檔案開啟，聆聽 MP3 內容。

Part 1 Photographs 照片描述

題型介紹

題數	六題（多益考試兩百題中的第 1~6 題）
題型說明	• 6 張照片印在試題本中。 • 聽完四個選項後，選出最符合照片的敘述。
題目時間間隔	約 5 秒
題目範例	🎧 Track 01 **錄音內容** (A) The businesspeople are looking at a plan. (B) The women are taking off their glasses. (C) The man on the left is picking up a mug. (D) The people are all listening to the radio. 正解 (A)

基本作答技巧

Step 1 播放 Listening Test 及 Part 1 作答說明（Directions）與範例（Example）時（考前應已熟悉各大題型及作答方式），先迅速瀏覽 6 張照片。

Step 2 聽到錄音播放 "Now Part 1 will begin." 時立即回到第一題的照片。

Step 3 聽到播放 "No. 1: Look at the picture marked No. 1 in your test book." 時專注於該張照片。

Step 4 每聽完一個選項，只要敘述內容與照片不符，腦中立即刪除該選項（先不必馬上填寫答案）。

Step 5 聽完四個選項後立即將正確答案畫在答案卡上（2 秒內畫完）。

Step 6 利用題目時間間隔所剩的 2~3 秒，接著看下一題照片。

Step 7 第 2~6 題依上述 Steps 3~6 的流程作答。

Part 1　Photographs

四大類照片題範例與解題技巧

範例 1：單人照
🎧 Track 02

📝 解題技巧

💡 注意該人物所做的動作（常用現在進行式）。

💡 刪去法要訣
　a. 若能大致確定其他三項有不正確處（如動作不符），就大膽選聽不懂的那一項。
　b. 若三項中有一項看似正確，則不要留戀聽不懂的第四項，大膽選下看似正確的一項。

錄音內容

(A) The man is fixing cars.
(B) The man is riding a bicycle.
(C) The man is standing by a bike.
(D) The man is speaking on a stage.

解析

➡ 修車，動作不符，🗑。
➡ 騎腳踏車，動作不符，🗑。
➡ 站在腳踏車旁，bike = bicycle，正確。
➡ 在台上演講，動作不符，🗑。

🎧 Track 03

Exercise

Listen to the audio track. Select the one statement that best describes what you see in the picture.

Your answer: Ⓐ Ⓑ Ⓒ Ⓓ

範例 2：多人照

🎧 *Track 04*

> 📝 **解題技巧**
>
> 💡 觀察其中人物（the men / the women / they / the people）動作的共通性及差異性。
>
> 💡 留意針對某一位（the man/woman）的動作或外觀描述是否相符。

錄音內容

(A) Both men are writing in notebooks.
(B) The people are moving the chairs.
(C) The woman is typing on a computer.
(D) The woman is handing the men some documents.

解析

➡ 男子並沒有在筆記本上寫字，🔇。
➡ 移動椅子，與所有人動作不符，🔇。
➡ 女子沒有在打字，🔇。
➡ 女子遞交文件給男子，正確。

🎧 *Track 05*

Exercise

Listen to the audio track. Select the one statement that best describes what you see in the picture.

Your answer: Ⓐ Ⓑ Ⓒ Ⓓ

Part 1 Photographs

範例 3：景物照

🎧 Track 06

📝 解題技巧

💡 留意周遭環境、景物狀態及地點。

💡 照片中若有人時，要注意人物與環境的關係。

💡 若用<u>現在完成式的被動語態</u>（have been + p.p.），表示該事物在照片中已呈現的狀態或擺放方式。

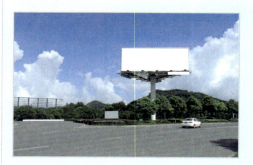

錄音內容

(A) There is a lot of traffic on the road.
(B) The car is stopped at a red light.
(C) Some people are waiting to cross the road.
(D) A billboard has been placed by the road.

解析

➡ 交通並不擁擠，與環境不符，❌。
➡ 車輛並沒有停在紅燈前，❌。
➡ 聽到主詞 some people 並對應照片中根本沒有人，即知不符，❌。
➡ 路旁有設置廣告看板（表已呈現的狀態），**正確**。

🎧 Track 07

Exercise

Listen to the audio track. Select the one statement that best describes what you see in the picture.

Your answer: Ⓐ Ⓑ Ⓒ Ⓓ

範例 4：物件照 　🎧 Track 08

📝 解題技巧

💡 留意物件的種類名稱、呈現的狀態和擺放位置及相對關係等。

💡 常考方位關係字詞

on / on top of 在……上面	under/underneath 在……下面
above/over 在……上方（沒有接觸到）	below/beneath 在……下方
in front of / before 在……前面	in back of / behind 在……後面
near/nearby 在……附近／旁	far from 離……很遠
next to / by 緊鄰	between A and B 在 A 和 B 之間

錄音內容

(A) There is a laptop next to the files.
(B) The documents have been arranged in a pile.
(C) The folders have been placed on the bookshelf.
(D) The stack of files is far from the phone.

解析

➡ 文件旁的不是筆電，錯。
➡ 文件成堆放置（現在完成式的被動，表呈現的狀態），正確。
➡ 檔案夾並不是放在書架上，而是在桌上，錯。
➡ 這堆文件並沒有離電話很遠，錯。

🎧 Track 09

Exercise

Listen to the audio track. Select the one statement that best describes what you see in the picture.

Your answer: Ⓐ Ⓑ Ⓒ Ⓓ

Part 1　Photographs

八大照片題之場景與搶分詞彙

以下整理 Part 1「照片描述」中的常見場景與重要詞彙，請將已學會的詞彙打 √（在其他聽力單元中也常會出現，考前務必要全部記起來），並經常聆聽，以熟悉各個詞彙的發音。

場景 1：辦公室 & 一般商務（Office & General Business）

🎧 Track 10

設施與物品	動詞（詞組）
☐ bulletin board 布告欄	☐ deliver a speech 演講
☐ cell phone / smartphone 手機／智慧型手機	☐ do paperwork 處理文書工作
☐ conference/meeting room 會議室	☐ give a presentation 做簡報
☐ desktop/laptop/tablet computer 桌上型／筆記型／平板電腦	☐ have/hold a meeting 開會
☐ file cabinet 檔案櫃	☐ pick up sth. 拿起某物
☐ (photo)copy machine / (photo)copier 影印機	☐ shake hands 握手
☐ projection screen 投影布幕	☐ staple documents 裝訂文件
☐ projector 投影機	☐ take seats 就座
☐ whiteboard 白板	☐ walk around (place)（在某處）走來走去
	☐ work at one's desk 在座位上工作

🎧 Track 11

Exercise

Listen to the audio track. Select the one statement that best describes what you see in the picture.

Your answer: Ⓐ Ⓑ Ⓒ Ⓓ

場景 2：房屋內外（Inside & Outside the House） *Track 12*

地點、設施與物品		動詞（詞組）
☐ balcony 陽台	☐ mailbox 信箱	☐ dispose (of) 處理掉
☐ carpet/rug 地毯	☐ patio 前廊；露台	☐ fix 修理
☐ ceiling 天花板	☐ porch 走廊	☐ mop/sweep the floor 拖／掃地
☐ cupboard 櫥櫃	☐ potted plants 盆栽植物	☐ plant (flowers/trees) 種植（花／樹木）
☐ driveway 車道	☐ sink 水槽	
☐ fence 籬笆	☐ steps/stairs/staircase 台階；樓梯	☐ prepare (food) 準備（食物）
☐ fireplace 壁爐		☐ put away sth. 收拾某物
☐ furniture 家具	☐ stove 火爐	☐ sew 縫
☐ garage 車庫	☐ tile 瓷磚	☐ sth. is being painted 某物在上油漆
☐ garden 花園	☐ vacuum cleaner 吸塵器	
☐ handrail/railing 欄杆；扶手	☐ vase 花瓶	☐ turn off 關掉（開關）
	☐ wallpaper 壁紙	☐ turn on 打開（開關）
☐ ladder 梯子		☐ wipe the table 擦桌子
☐ laundry 待洗衣物		

Track 13

Exercise

Listen to the audio track. Select the one statement that best describes what you see in the picture.

Your answer: Ⓐ Ⓑ Ⓒ Ⓓ

Part 1 Photographs

場景 3：餐廳 & 旅館（Restaurant & Hotel） 🎧 Track 14

	地點與人物	物品	動詞（詞組）
餐廳	☐ chef/cook 廚師 ☐ host/hostess （男／女）領台 ☐ waiter/waitress （男／女）服務生 ☐ waiting area 等候帶位處	☐ bill 帳單 ☐ menu 菜單 ☐ tablecloth 桌巾 ☐ tableware 餐具	☐ have (a meal) 用餐 ☐ order one's meal 點餐 ☐ serve (food) 上菜 ☐ set the table 擺放餐具
旅館	☐ front desk 櫃台 ☐ hotel room 客房 ☐ lobby 大廳 ☐ bellboy/bellhop （旅館）行李員 ☐ doorman/porter 門房 ☐ front-desk clerk 櫃台人員 ☐ maid（女）清潔員	☐ bed linen 床單 ☐ bedspread 床罩 ☐ lamp 燈 ☐ nightstand / night table 床頭桌 ☐ pillow 枕頭 ☐ room service menu 客房服務菜單 ☐ safe 保險箱	☐ change the sheets 更換床單 ☐ check in 住房 ☐ check out 退房 ☐ do housekeeping 房務整理 ☐ make the bed 鋪床 ☐ make up the room 整理房間

🎧 Track 15

Exercise

Listen to the audio track. Select the one statement that best describes what you see in the picture.

Your answer: Ⓐ Ⓑ Ⓒ Ⓓ

場景 4：商店（Stores）

🎧 Track 16

人物
☐ cashier 收銀員
☐ customer/shopper 顧客
☐ owner 老闆
☐ salesperson 銷售員
☐ vendor 小販

地點與物品
☐ (book) cart （店員暫時擺放或整理書籍的）推車
☐ bookshelf 書架
☐ cash register 收銀台
☐ (check-out) counter 結帳櫃台
☐ clothing 衣物
☐ grocery 食品雜貨
☐ merchandise 商品
☐ shopping cart 購物車

動詞（詞組）
☐ be arranged in a row/pile 排成一列／一堆
☐ be on sale 待售；拍賣
☐ be piled up 堆成一疊
☐ be stacked on 堆疊在……上
☐ buy/purchase 購買
☐ have a sale 折扣賣出
☐ ring sth. up 物品結帳
☐ set up (tables/chairs) 排放（桌椅等）
☐ sth. is displayed 展示某物
☐ sth. is lined up 排列物品
☐ sth. has fallen over 某物倒下
☐ try on 試穿

🎧 Track 17

Exercise

Listen to the audio track. Select the one statement that best describes what you see in the picture.

Your answer: Ⓐ Ⓑ Ⓒ Ⓓ

場景 5：大眾運輸（Public Transportation） Track 18

人物	物品
☐ captain/pilot 機（船）長	☐ baggage/luggage/suitcase 行李
☐ commuter 通勤者	☐ boarding pass 登機證
☐ customs officer 海關人員	☐ luggage cart/trolley 行李推車
☐ flight attendant 空服員	☐ passport 護照
☐ passenger 乘客	☐ refreshments 機上餐點
☐ travel agent 旅行業者	

地點與交通工具	動詞（詞組）
☐ airport 機場	☐ board 登機
☐ cruise 航遊；遊輪	☐ claim (luggage) 取得（行李）
☐ check-in counter 行李託運櫃台	☐ get in the (car/taxi) 上（轎車／計程車等小型交通工具）
☐ ferry 渡輪	
☐ gate 登機門	☐ get on the (train/bus/boat) 上（火車／公車／船等大型交通工具）
☐ shuttle 接駁車；往返固定兩地之短程交通工具	☐ land 降落
☐ subway 地鐵	☐ take off 起飛
☐ terminal 航廈	☐ wait in line 排隊等候

Track 19

Exercise

Listen to the audio track. Select the one statement that best describes what you see in the picture.

Your answer: Ⓐ Ⓑ Ⓒ Ⓓ

場景 6：建築工地 & 公共設施（Construction Site & Public Infrastructure） 🎧 Track 20

	物品或地點	人物或動詞（詞組）
建築工地	☐ blueprint/plan 藍圖 ☐ crane 起重機 ☐ frame 骨架 ☐ construction/hard hat 工地帽 ☐ lumber/timber/log 木材 ☐ machinery 機具 ☐ steel 鋼鐵	☐ carpenter 木匠 ☐ construction worker 建築工人 ☐ build/construct 建造 ☐ operate (machinery) 運轉（機械等） ☐ point 指向 ☐ remove 移除 ☐ supervise 監督
公共設施	☐ bicycle rack 自行車架 ☐ highway/freeway 高速公路 ☐ intersection 十字路口 ☐ pavement/sidewalk 人行道 ☐ toll booth 收費站 ☐ traffic light 紅綠燈	☐ pedestrian 行人 ☐ make a stop 暫時停車 ☐ pave 鋪路 ☐ ship 運送貨物包裹 ☐ step out of 走出 ☐ walk 步行

🎧 Track 21

Exercise

Listen to the audio track. Select the one statement that best describes what you see in the picture.

Your answer: Ⓐ Ⓑ Ⓒ Ⓓ

場景 7：戶外 & 運動相關（Outdoors & Sports）

🎧 Track 22

物品或地點	人物或活動
☐ dock 碼頭	☐ diving 潛水
☐ fishing gear 釣魚用具	☐ fisherman 漁夫
☐ horizon 地平線	☐ fishing 釣魚
☐ landscape/scenery 風景	☐ hiking 健行
☐ lighthouse 燈塔	☐ mountain climbing 登山
☐ offshore 離岸	☐ park ranger 公園管理者
☐ on shore 在岸上	☐ skiing 滑雪
☐ (river)bank 河岸	☐ stroll = take a stroll/walk 散步
☐ goggles 蛙鏡	☐ athlete 運動員
☐ gym 健身房；體育館	☐ jogger 慢跑者
☐ sweatshirt 運動長衫	☐ jogging 慢跑
☐ (swimming) pool 泳池	☐ play tennis 打網球
☐ tennis ball 網球	☐ work out / exercise 運動
☐ tennis court 網球場	
☐ tennis racket 網球拍	

(左欄：戶外；右欄：運動相關)

🎧 Track 23

Exercise

Listen to the audio track. Select the one statement that best describes what you see in the picture.

Your answer: Ⓐ Ⓑ Ⓒ Ⓓ

場景 8：醫院 & 診所（Hospital & Clinic） 🎧 Track 24

人物	醫療相關
☐ dentist 牙醫	☐ administer (medicine) 給（藥）
☐ doctor 醫生	☐ bandage 繃帶
☐ eye doctor 眼科醫生	☐ blood pressure 血壓
☐ (lab) technician（實驗室）技術人員	☐ check up on / examine 檢查
☐ nurse 護士	☐ give a shot 打針
☐ patient 病患	☐ medical report 醫療報告
☐ vet = veterinarian 獸醫	☐ pill/medicine 藥
地點	☐ prescribe 開藥方
☐ emergency room 急診室	☐ prescription 處方籤
☐ examination room 診療室	☐ stethoscope 聽診器
☐ laboratory 實驗室	☐ surgery 手術
☐ pharmacy/drugstore 藥局	☐ symptom 症狀
☐ waiting room 候診室	☐ thermometer 溫度計
	☐ x-ray X光片

🎧 Track 25

Exercise

Listen to the audio track. Select the one statement that best describes what you see in the picture.

Your answer: Ⓐ Ⓑ Ⓒ Ⓓ

Part 1 Photographs

Practice Test PART 1

Directions:

For each question in this part, you will hear four statements about a picture in your test book. When you hear the statements, you must select the one statement that best describes what you see in the picture. Then find the number of the question on your answer sheet and mark your answer. The statements will not be printed in your test book and will be spoken only one time.

Track 26

1.

Your answer: Ⓐ Ⓑ Ⓒ Ⓓ

2.

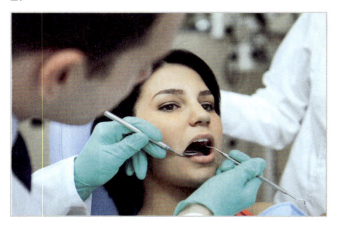

Your answer: Ⓐ Ⓑ Ⓒ Ⓓ

3.

Your answer: Ⓐ Ⓑ Ⓒ Ⓓ

4.

Your answer: Ⓐ Ⓑ Ⓒ Ⓓ

Part 1 照片描述

Part 1 Photographs

5.

Your answer: Ⓐ Ⓑ Ⓒ Ⓓ

6.

Your answer: Ⓐ Ⓑ Ⓒ Ⓓ

Part 2　Question and Response 應答問題

題型介紹

題數	二十五題（多益考試兩百題中的第 7~31 題）
題型說明	• 問題及選項皆<u>不出現</u>在試題本中。 • 聽完問題及三個選項後選出最適當的回應。
題目時間間隔	約 5 秒
題目範例	🎧 Track 27 **錄音內容** Q: How will you get to work tomorrow? 　(A) I've been there for three years. 　(B) I'll ride my bicycle. 　(C) I'll take a break later. 正解 (B)

基本作答技巧

Tip 1 關鍵字詞 確認題型	注意聽題目開頭並辨識題型（詳見 p.30~31），便可輕鬆選出答案（主要題型如右）。	Wh-Questions 疑問詞疑問句 Yes/No Questions 是非問句 A or B Questions 選擇疑問句 Statements 直述句
Tip 2 不要掉入陷阱	選項中常用同音、近音或同義詞等來混淆考生，有這類情況時 **95%** 都<u>不是</u>標準答案。	同音 例 wait/weight、meet/meat 近音 例 walk/work、staff/stuff 同義 例 coworker/colleague、client/customer/shopper
Tip 3 掌握分析答案	含有類似右列之「模糊回答」，因在邏輯上往往都說得通，因此通常都是對的選項。	Ⓐ 表「不確定／不清楚」 例 I'm not sure. 我不確定耶。 　 I don't know. / I have no idea. 不知道。 Ⓑ 表「再作確認／查詢」 例 Let me think about it. 我想想看。 　 Let me check. 我查查看。 　 Let me ask someone. 我問一下別人。

Part 2　Question and Response

題型分析圖

START

是否以疑問詞「5W1H」開頭？

是

題型 1　Wh- questions
疑問詞疑問句
出題頻率約 50%

開頭為：When、Where、Who/Whose

When 找「時間」：
- 例 幾點幾分、一天中的某時段、星期幾或日期等。

Where 找「地點」：
- 例 某人家、家具上或容器內、辦公室、商店、建築物等。

Who/Whose 找「人」：
- 例 人名、姓氏、職稱或身份關係等。

開頭為：Which/What

Which/What + 名詞：
注意聽此名詞為何。
- 例 Which **country**、What **color** 等？

What + 助動詞：
不理助動詞，而抓出問句中之**動詞**。
- 例 What do you **think/like** …？（問想法）

開頭為：How

How + 助動詞：
注意聽**動詞**為何。
- 例 How do you **like** …？（問感覺）
  How did (sth.) **go**？（問事情進展）

How + 形容詞／副詞：
- 例 How much …？（問多少錢）
  How often …？（問發生頻率）

How about + Ving：
提議或邀請。
- 例 How about going …？（問要不要去……）

開頭為：Why

詢問原因：
答案可能含 because/since/as 等表原因的連接詞，但亦可省略。

提出建議：
- 例 Why don't you …？

30

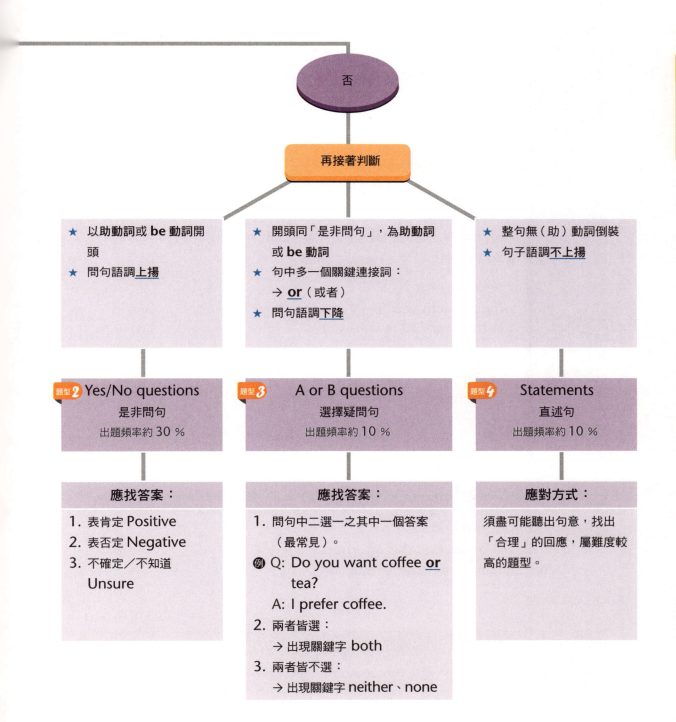

題型 1 Wh- questions   Ⓐ When 問「時間」

回應與「時間」有關，如： 🎧 Track 28

時間	• at 6 (o'clock) 在六點 • at 7 a.m./p.m. 在上午／下午七點 • at noon/midnight 在中午／午夜 • in an/one hour 一小時後 • between ten and twelve / from ten to twelve 在十點到十二點之間 • this/tomorrow afternoon 今天／明天下午
星期幾	• on Friday 在星期五 • by next Wednesday 下週三前
月份或 日期	• in January 在一月 • on the second of December 在十二月二號 • by the end of the week 本週結束前
年份	• next year 明年 • the previous year 前一年 • in (the year) 2014 二〇一四年
某時間點	• before/after lunch 在午餐前／後 • as soon as 一……時 • while/when 在……的同時 • two years ago 兩年前

Example
🎧 Track 29

Q <u>When</u> can I have those reports?　　說明▶ 問 When 找「時間」關鍵字。

(A) Just press this button.
(B) They will be finished this **afternoon**.
(C) You can find them at the restaurant.

🎧 Track 30

Exercise

Listen to the audio track and select the best response to the question or statement.

1. Your answer: Ⓐ Ⓑ Ⓒ
2. Your answer: Ⓐ Ⓑ Ⓒ
3. Your answer: Ⓐ Ⓑ Ⓒ

題型 1　Wh- questions　B Where 問「地點」

回應與「某一地點或場所」有關，如：　　🎧 Track 31

置物容器或器具	• in the pocket 在口袋裡 • in the container 在保鮮盒／罐子裡 • in the backpack/handbag 在包包裡 • in the briefcase/suitcase 在公事包／行李箱裡
家具	• on the desk/chair/sofa/couch 在桌子／椅子／沙發上 • in the cabinet/cupboard 在櫃子裡
建築物	• in the (main) office 在辦公室裡 • in the factory/warehouse 在工廠／倉庫 • on the second floor 在二樓
商家店面	• at the mall downtown 在市中心的購物中心 • at the new store next to the library 在圖書館旁新開的那家店
公共設施	• in the playground 在操場／遊戲場 • at the museum/gallery 在博物館／美術館 • near the city hall 在市政廳附近
其他	• over there 在那邊 • down the hall 走廊那頭 • across the street 在對街 • (to) my home address 送到我家

Example　🎧 Track 32

Q **Where** could I buy a jacket like that?　　說明▶ 問 Where 找「地點」關鍵字。

A (A) Jack is getting a promotion.
　　(B) It should leave at 8:30 tonight.
　　(C) At the **department store** next to the city hall.

🎧 Track 33

Exercise

Listen to the audio track and select the best response to the question or statement.

1. Your answer: Ⓐ Ⓑ Ⓒ
2. Your answer: Ⓐ Ⓑ Ⓒ
3. Your answer: Ⓐ Ⓑ Ⓒ

題型 1 Wh- questions C Who/Whose 問「人」

答案與「人」有關，包括人名、姓氏、對象、職稱或身份關係等。如： 🎧 Track 34

稱謂 + 姓氏	• Mr. Sanchez/Miller/Dean/Lee/Chang（某某先生） • Mrs./Ms. Smith/Kim/Yem/Brown/Robinson（某某女士）
人名	• Jim/Mario/Chuck/Kenichi（男子名） • Mary/Sarah/Melissa/Kumiko（女子名）
關係	• coworker/colleague 同事 • boss/manager/supervisor 上司 • customer/client 客戶 • classmate 同學 • roommate 室友
部門	• sales/marketing department 業務／行銷部 • human resources department 人資部（簡稱為 HR） • customer service department 客服部
職業	• lawyer 律師　　• secretary 秘書 • journalist 記者　• doctor 醫生（常用稱謂如 Dr. Jackson）
所有格代名詞	單數：mine 我的　yours 你的　his 他的　hers 她的 複數：ours 我們的　yours 你們的　theirs 他們的

Example
🎧 Track 35

Q <u>Who</u> should I send the letter to?　　說明 問 Who 找與「人物」相關的答案。

A (A) You should give them my address.
(B) Tell them it is for a good cause.
(C) Mail it to **Mr. Steve Timpson**.

🎧 Track 36

Exercise

Listen to the audio track and select the best response to the question or statement.

1. Your answer: Ⓐ Ⓑ Ⓒ
2. Your answer: Ⓐ Ⓑ Ⓒ
3. Your answer: Ⓐ Ⓑ Ⓒ

題型 1　Wh- questions　Ⓓ Which/What 問「何者／什麼」

第一類

🎧 Track 37

Which / What + N.
說明 注意聽此名詞為何。

例 Q: Which **car** will Sam be driving?
　A: His company car.

例 Q: What **days** do you exercise?
　A: Only on Saturdays.

第二類

🎧 Track 38

What + 助動詞
說明 不理助動詞，抓出問句中之動詞。

例 Q: What should I **wear** for my interview?
　A: A shirt and tie.

其他常考句型

🎧 Track 39

What time 問幾點

例 Q: **What time** is our afternoon break?
　A: 3:30 p.m.

What + V.（過去式）
說明 這類問題不像上述兩類基本句型，僅須注意 What 之後的名詞或動詞為何即可從容作答。What + V. 題型在聽出問題後，還常須了解選項的整體句意才能找出合理的回應，屬高難度題型，作答時須集中火力仔細聆聽每一個選項。

例 Q: **What happened** to your car?
　A: It got a flat tire.

例 Q: **What went wrong** with the machine?
　A: I think it wasn't used properly.

例 Q: **What went through her mind**?
　A: She was thinking about the new project.

例 Q: **What took you so long** to arrive?
　A: My car broke down on my way here.

🎧 Track 40

Exercise

Listen to the audio track and select the best response to the question or statement.

1. Your answer: Ⓐ Ⓑ Ⓒ
2. Your answer: Ⓐ Ⓑ Ⓒ
3. Your answer: Ⓐ Ⓑ Ⓒ

Part 2 Question and Response

題型 1 Wh- questions — E How 問「方法、狀態、程度或意願」

第一類
🎧 Track 41

How + 助動詞
說明 不理助動詞,注意聽問句中之**動詞**。

例 Q: How **do** you **like** your coffee?
A: Black with no sugar.

第二類
🎧 Track 42

How + 形容詞／副詞
• How much 多少錢
• How often 多常（頻率）
• How long 時間或長度
• How good/well/bad 多好／多壞（問程度）

例 Q: **How much** is that MP3 player?
A: 200 dollars plus tax.

例 Q: **How long** have you studied German?
A: Roughly half a year.

大補帖 問 How often 時,常以「頻率副詞」作回應,常用的包括:always「總是」、usually「經常」、often「時常」、sometimes「有時候」、once in a while「有時」、rarely「很少」、never「從不」。

問 How long 時,除了回答時間有多長之外,也可能是問「長度」。常用的長度單位有:kilometer(s)「公里」、meter(s)「公尺」、centimeter(s)「公分」、mile(s)「英里」、foot/feet「英尺」、inch(es)「英吋」、yard(s)「碼」。

第三類
🎧 Track 43

How about + Ving
說明 表提議或邀請。How about 後亦可接子句、名詞或名詞片語。

例 Q: **How about going** to lunch together after the meeting?
A: Great. I know there's a good Italian restaurant nearby.

🎧 Track 44

Exercise

Listen to the audio track and select the best response to the question or statement.

1. Your answer: Ⓐ Ⓑ Ⓒ
2. Your answer: Ⓐ Ⓑ Ⓒ
3. Your answer: Ⓐ Ⓑ Ⓒ

題型 1　Wh- questions　**F** Why 問「原因」或表「提議」

問「原因」

🎧 Track 45

Why + 助動詞／be 動詞

例 Q: Why did you **close** your **account**?
A: (Because) the service charges were too high.

例 Q: Why isn't the office open next Monday?
A: It's a holiday.

小撇步
1. 以 Why 開頭問「原因」時須了解問題及所有選項之內容大意，注意所有動詞、其時態及基本受詞等，屬高難度題型。
2. 回應時 because/since/as 等表原因的連接詞可省略。

表「提議」

🎧 Track 46

Why don't { you / I / we } ...

表接受或贊同：
例 Q: Why don't you stay and have dinner with us?
A: That would be great.

表拒絕：
例 Q: Why don't we go to the mall after work?
A: I can't. I have to work overtime.

小提醒 以 why 開頭接 don't/doesn't 表提出建議時，屬於「隱藏式 why 問句」，不是要問對方原因，而是提供建議或提議，適當的回應通常只有兩種：即對建議表示「贊同」或「不贊同」。

🎧 Track 47

Exercise

Listen to the audio track and select the best response to the question or statement.

1. Your answer: Ⓐ Ⓑ Ⓒ
2. Your answer: Ⓐ Ⓑ Ⓒ
3. Your answer: Ⓐ Ⓑ Ⓒ

Part 2 Question and Response

題型 2　Yes/No Questions　是非問句

辨識法一：以助動詞或 be 動詞開頭

🎧 Track 48

肯定	否定	範例
Is Was Are Were	Isn't Wasn't Aren't Weren't	Q: Is there a drugstore nearby? A: There's one across from the park. Q: Aren't there any seats available? A: No, not at the moment. 說明▶ 否定疑問句回答方式與肯定一樣（可忽略否定部分想成是肯定句，會較容易理解與回答），也可以 Yes/No 回答。
Do Does Did	Don't Doesn't Didn't	Q: Did you hear Craig is Employee of the Month? A: Really? He won it last month, too.
Have Has Had	Haven't Hasn't Hadn't	Q: Have you ever been to France? A: I went when I was a child.
Will Would	Won't Wouldn't	Q: Would you like a window seat? A: I would prefer one by the aisle.
Can Could	Can't Couldn't	Q: Can I print this document? A: Sure, but please wait five minutes.
Should Shall	Shouldn't	Q: Should we order some more staples? A: No, we already have a lot.

辨識法二：問句語調上揚

問句語調上揚是 Yes/No Questions「是非問句」的獨有特色。而「是非問句」中夾雜 Wh- 疑問詞時，即為「間接問句」。

一般是非問句 vs. 間接問句

🎧 Track 49

一般是非問句	間接問句
Q: Was that movie you saw on the weekend any good? A: Yes, I really enjoyed it.	Q: Do you have any idea **when** the new *Iron Man* movie will be on DVD? A: Probably next week.

📝 小撇步　注意聽中間的 **Wh-** 疑問詞為何，為回應答案的關鍵。

Yes/No Questions 重要觀念

🎧 Track 50

單行道原則	範例與說明
Yes/No Questions 不一定以 Yes/No 回答（即 Yes/No 二字可被省略） | Q	A
Yes/No Questions	Yes, . . . No, . . . 開頭沒有 Yes/No		Q: Are there any good schools near here? A: 肯定 Yes, there are several, but they are expensive. 　否定 No, there aren't any outstanding ones nearby. ▶ Yes/No 都可能省略掉，卻不影響句意，變成： A: 肯定 There are several, but they are expensive. 　否定 There aren't any outstanding ones nearby.
以 Yes/No 開頭的答案選項一定只能對應 Yes/No Questions！	Q: **Where** do you keep your knives and forks? A: (A) **Yes**, they are in the bathroom. 　(B) **No**, they aren't on the shelf. 　(C) In the kitchen cupboard.

小撇步 以 Yes/No 開頭的答案選項 (A) 和 (B)，不可能對應本題的 Wh- Question，故一定不是正確答案。

Q	A
Yes/No Questions ◀ONE WAY 非 Yes/No Questions 如： • Wh- Questions • A or B Questions • Statements	Yes, . . . No, . . .

🎧 Track 51

Exercise

Listen to the audio track and select the best response to the question or statement.

1. Your answer: Ⓐ Ⓑ Ⓒ
2. Your answer: Ⓐ Ⓑ Ⓒ
3. Your answer: Ⓐ Ⓑ Ⓒ

題型 2 隱藏式 Yes/No Questions　附加問句 Tag Question

句型與範例

🎧 Track 52

主要子句	附加問句	
S. + V. ,	助動詞／be 動詞 + (not)	代名詞？
肯定直述句（＋）	否定附加問句（－）	
Martin is the project manager,	isn't he?	
Karen can speak five languages,	can't she?	
The managers will fly to Japan,	won't they?	
Kevin swims every day after work,	doesn't he?	說明 主要子句為一般動詞時，附加問句要用助動詞 do、does、did 來表示。
You just got back from a business trip,	didn't you?	
Lily has finished the report,	hasn't she?	
You would prefer to stay at a hotel downtown,	wouldn't you?	
否定直述句（－）	肯定附加問句（＋）	
You aren't going to stay with us,	are you?	
This is not the picture Mr. Lee chose,	is it?	
He wasn't a real insurance salesman,	was he?	
You didn't play video games all day,	did you?	
Sally won't forget to come to the party,	will she?	

> 📖 注意
> 1. 句子最後**語調上揚**，得知「附加問句」亦屬「是非問句」的一種。
> 2. 附加問句與主要子句的**動詞一致**。
> 3. 否定的附加問句通常**以縮寫表示**。

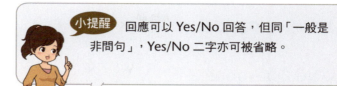
小提醒 回應可以 Yes/No 回答，但同「一般是非問句」，Yes/No 二字亦可被省略。

可能的回應

肯定	否定
Yes, he is.	No, he isn't.
Yes, she's really talented.	No, she can only speak two.
Yes, they will go there next week.	No, the trip was canceled.
I think so. Exercise is important to him.	I think he only swims on Wednesdays.
You're right. I just came back last night.	I went on that trip weeks ago!
Of course! She gave it to me this morning.	Actually, she said she needs more time.
Yeah, I think that would be more convenient.	Not really. I'd rather stay near the beach.

否定	肯定
Don't worry. I'm staying with my aunt.	You told me before that I could!
No, he chose a different one.	Yes, that's the one he wanted.
No, I don't think he was.	As far as I know, he does sell insurance.
No, I did my homework and cleaned the house.	Yes, but I didn't have anything else to do!
No way! She won't want to miss it.	Probably. She never remembers anything.

Track 53

Exercise

Listen to the audio track and select the best response to the question or statement.

1. Your answer: Ⓐ Ⓑ Ⓒ
2. Your answer: Ⓐ Ⓑ Ⓒ
3. Your answer: Ⓐ Ⓑ Ⓒ

題型 3 A or B Questions 選擇疑問句

是非問句 vs. 選擇疑問句

Yes/No Questions 是非問句
- 問句語調上揚

共通
- 以助動詞或 be 動詞開頭

A or B Questions 選擇疑問句
- 問句語調下降
- 句中多一個關鍵連接詞：or「或者」

在正確辨識出「選擇疑問句」題型後，可以期待下列三者之一為答案： 🎧 Track 54

出現頻率	答案類型	可能出現字
高	二選一之其中一個答案	二選一之其中一個字詞

Q: Is your flight on **Monday** **or** **Tuesday**?
A: I'll leave on **Monday** at 7 o'clock sharp.

中	兩者皆選	關鍵字 both 或 either

Q: Do you prefer the **yellow sweater** **or** the **black one**?
A: Actually, I like them **both**.

中	兩者皆不選	關鍵字 neither 或 none

Q: Do you prefer the **gray shirt** **or** the **black one**?
A: **Neither**. I don't like dark colors.

🎧 Track 55

Exercise

Listen to the audio track and select the best response to the question or statement.

1. Your answer: Ⓐ Ⓑ Ⓒ
2. Your answer: Ⓐ Ⓑ Ⓒ
3. Your answer: Ⓐ Ⓑ Ⓒ

題型 4　Statements　直述句

「直述句」屬高難度考題，為 Part 2 中唯一非問句的題型。

應對技巧

1. 需要「了解越多資訊越好」，平日需多做練習，培養「聽」的實力。
2. 找出合常理或符合邏輯的回應。

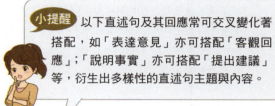

小提醒 以下直述句及其回應常可交叉變化著搭配，如「表達意見」亦可搭配「客觀回應」;「說明事實」亦可搭配「提出建議」等，衍生出多樣性的直述句主題與內容。

常見型態：　　🎧 Track 56

直述句	回應
陳述或說明事實	**表達想法或作法**
Some potential clients are coming to meet us next Monday.	I look forward to seeing them.
Mr. Kidman has pushed back the deadline for the budget report.	Then I can work on it at home this weekend.
The new store hasn't been as profitable as we had hoped.	Given that the economy is doing poorly now, I'm not surprised.
表達感受	**提出建議／客觀回應**
The carpet of this hotel room is so dirty.	Maybe we should call housekeeping.
It's been uncomfortably humid these past couple of days.	The temperature has been higher this summer.
表達意見	**延伸想法或結果**
I think cutting back some workers' hours will save the company a lot of money.	It might also increase individual productivity!

🎧 Track 57

Exercise

Listen to the audio track and select the best response to the question or statement.

1. Your answer: Ⓐ Ⓑ Ⓒ
2. Your answer: Ⓐ Ⓑ Ⓒ
3. Your answer: Ⓐ Ⓑ Ⓒ

Part 2 Question and Response

Practice Test PART 2

Directions:
You will hear a question or statement and three responses spoken in English. They will not be printed in your test book and will be spoken only one time. Select the best response to the question or statement and mark the letter (A), (B), or (C) on your answer sheet.

🎧 Track 58

1. Mark your answer on your answer sheet.
2. Mark your answer on your answer sheet.
3. Mark your answer on your answer sheet.
4. Mark your answer on your answer sheet.
5. Mark your answer on your answer sheet.
6. Mark your answer on your answer sheet.
7. Mark your answer on your answer sheet.
8. Mark your answer on your answer sheet.
9. Mark your answer on your answer sheet.
10. Mark your answer on your answer sheet.
11. Mark your answer on your answer sheet.
12. Mark your answer on your answer sheet.
13. Mark your answer on your answer sheet.
14. Mark your answer on your answer sheet.
15. Mark your answer on your answer sheet.
16. Mark your answer on your answer sheet.
17. Mark your answer on your answer sheet.
18. Mark your answer on your answer sheet.
19. Mark your answer on your answer sheet.
20. Mark your answer on your answer sheet.
21. Mark your answer on your answer sheet.
22. Mark your answer on your answer sheet.
23. Mark your answer on your answer sheet.
24. Mark your answer on your answer sheet.
25. Mark your answer on your answer sheet.

No.	ANSWER A B C	No.	ANSWER A B C	No.	ANSWER A B C	No.	ANSWER A B C	No.	ANSWER A B C
1	Ⓐ Ⓑ Ⓒ	6	Ⓐ Ⓑ Ⓒ	11	Ⓐ Ⓑ Ⓒ	16	Ⓐ Ⓑ Ⓒ	21	Ⓐ Ⓑ Ⓒ
2	Ⓐ Ⓑ Ⓒ	7	Ⓐ Ⓑ Ⓒ	12	Ⓐ Ⓑ Ⓒ	17	Ⓐ Ⓑ Ⓒ	22	Ⓐ Ⓑ Ⓒ
3	Ⓐ Ⓑ Ⓒ	8	Ⓐ Ⓑ Ⓒ	13	Ⓐ Ⓑ Ⓒ	18	Ⓐ Ⓑ Ⓒ	23	Ⓐ Ⓑ Ⓒ
4	Ⓐ Ⓑ Ⓒ	9	Ⓐ Ⓑ Ⓒ	14	Ⓐ Ⓑ Ⓒ	19	Ⓐ Ⓑ Ⓒ	24	Ⓐ Ⓑ Ⓒ
5	Ⓐ Ⓑ Ⓒ	10	Ⓐ Ⓑ Ⓒ	15	Ⓐ Ⓑ Ⓒ	20	Ⓐ Ⓑ Ⓒ	25	Ⓐ Ⓑ Ⓒ

Part 3 Short Conversations 簡短對話

題型介紹

題數	三十九題（多益考試兩百題中的第 32~70 題）
題型說明	• 會聽到 13 組兩個人或是三個人之間的簡短對話。 • 每組對話各有三個問題，13 組對話共 39 題。 • 每題組的**問題和答案選項都出現在題本中**。
題目時間間隔	約 7~8 秒
題目範例	🎧 Track 59 1. Where does the conversation most likely take place? 　(A) At the **airport security check** 　(B) On an **airplane** before takeoff 　(C) At an **airline counter** in the airport 　(D) In a taxi to the airport 2. Which **flight** is the woman going to take? 　(A) Flight J3253 to Dubai 　(B) Flight K3153 to Dublin 　(C) Flight A3153 to Dubai 　(D) Flight C3253 to Dublin 3. **How many bags** does the woman **check in**? 　(A) None 　(B) One 　(C) Two 　(D) Three 正解 1.(C) 2.(B) 3.(B)

基本作答流程與技巧

Step 1 瀏覽題目及選項
利用一開始播放 Direction 的時間瀏覽第一個題組的題目及選項，並推測可能的對話主題。

由左方題目及選項中的粗體關鍵字如 airport security check、airplane、airline counter、flight 及 how many bags . . . check in 等可推知對話主題可能與**搭機**有關。

Step 2 確認題型並找出問題點
聆聽對話錄音內容時，將注意力集中在三道題目的問題點上，並辨識應立即作答的題目（詳見 p.46 及 p.52~53）。

Step 3 預覽下一道題組
在各題組第三道題目唸完的同時，應已完成該題組的作答。然後利用與下一題組間的 7~8 秒時間，瀏覽下一個題組的題目及選項，並同樣推測對話主題與找出問題重點。

Part 3 Short Conversations

Part 3 應考概念與技巧

1. 對話模式多樣化

對話大多以**男女互相交談**的方式進行。除原本的兩人對話（如右範例），自 2018 年 3 月起新增三人對話或於對話中加入圖表（新題型說明及範例請見 p.56~59）。

範例（以下為 p.45「題目範例」的錄音內容）

Questions 1 through 3 refer to the following conversation.

M: Hello, ma'am. How can I help you today?

W: I'd like to check in, please. **Flight K3153 to Dublin**.

M: Do you have any luggage to check in?

W: Just this one. My luggage will be checked through to my final destination, right?

2. 字可能重複

不同於 Part 2「應答問題」，Part 3「簡短對話」中的答案是可以跟對話中所使用的字**一模一樣**的。即這裡比較不會有同音、近音字的陷阱問題。然而，同義字詞的替換仍是出題的主要方式之一，因此平時應多記（如右頁所列）。

範例（以 p.45 的「題目範例」Q2 為例）

Which flight is the woman going to take?
(A) Flight J3253 to Dubai
(B) **Flight K3153 to Dublin**
(C) Flight A3153 to Dubai
(D) Flight C3253 to Dublin

> 只要仔細聆聽對話內容即可找出答案。

3. 辨識應立即作答的題目

詢問相關細節問題（即 specific questions）一聽到對話中提及就應立即作答，否則很容易會忘掉該題的答案。這類問題的答案選項通常都很短，包括：

- 數字、個數（number）
- 人名（name）
- 時間／日期（time/date）
- 地名（location）

範例（以 p.45 的「題目範例」Q3 為例）

How many bags does the woman check in?
(A) None
(B) One
(C) Two
(D) Three

> 事先預覽題目時即注意到問「託運幾件行李」，因此聽到對話中問：「Do you have . . . check in?」便要仔細聆聽另一人的回應。由對話中女子說：「Just this one.」可知她只有一件要託運的行李。

> **小提醒** 雖說要立即作答，但建議僅先在答案卡上畫個小撇或打勾（如 Ⓐ Ⓑ ✓ Ⓓ 或 Ⓐ Ⓑ ╱ Ⓓ），待此段對話聽完後再完整地將答案畫滿（即 ●），以免在中途畫卡時漏聽了對話內容。

多益常考同義字

注意 → 所列出的字中，有些屬於意思相近的字，並非完全可以互相替換使用的　　🎧 Track 60

動詞	
整理、安排	arrange / set / settle / fix
幫助、協助	assist / help / give a hand
加入、參加	join / participate
取得	acquire / gain / get / obtain
聯繫	contact / get in touch with
結束	adjourn / end / finish
購買	buy / purchase
波動、變動	change / fluctuate / vary
捐贈、貢獻	contribute / donate / give away
依賴	count on / depend on / rely on
修理	fix / repair
管理、經營	handle / manage / run

名詞	
垃圾、廢棄物	garbage / trash / waste
商品、產品類	goods / merchandise / product / commodity
商人、賣家	merchant / seller / store owner / vendor
顧客、客人	client / consumer / customer / shopper
同事、工作夥伴	colleague / coworker / (business) partner
會議	meeting / conference / convention / seminar
展覽	exhibition / exhibit / fair / show
意見、想法	advice / opinion / thought / perspective
團員、成員、員工	staff / crew / team member / personnel / employee
領導者	president / leader / head / supervisor
美術館、博物館	gallery / museum

Part 3　Short Conversations

Part 3 的題型大多以 Wh- 形式的問句為主，包括人物、地點、談論主題、談話的細節內容等。常考題型分為四大類：

題型 1　與「人物」有關

常考問題	解題技巧
a. 問人物身份 • Who is sb.?	💡 注意聽人名，並於對話中找出其身份。
• What is the man's/woman's job/occupation? • What line of work is the man/woman in? • What type of job/business does the man/woman have?	💡 詢問某人的職業及工作性質時，可從對話中所談及的工作內容或相關專業詞彙來推斷。
b. 問人物間的關係： • What is the man and woman's relationship? • What is the relationship between the speakers?	💡 可從兩人對彼此的稱呼及談話內容等來掌握可能的訊息。

Example 1
🎧 Track 61

Q Who is **Christina**?

(A) The man's wife
(B) The woman's friend
(C) The man's colleague
(D) The woman's boss

錄音內容	解析
W: Are we still going to go to **Christina's** party tonight? I'm not sure I'm in the mood. M: Well, it has been a long week, I agree. But **she is one of your oldest friends**. W: I guess you're right, but I'm sure she'd understand if we didn't go. M: Well, I think we should, and if we get too tired, we can always come back early.	• 留心聽題目中的人名。 • 由男子對女子說：「她是妳認識最久的朋友之一」可知答案選 (B)。

說明 • 預先瀏覽題目時，注意問題中所詢問的人名，並在對話中仔細聆聽。
• 由選項可推知要找出 Christina 與對話男女的關係為何。

48

Example 2

🎧 Track 62

Q What is the relationship between the two speakers?

(A) They are relatives.
(B) They are old friends.
(C) They are coworkers.
(D) They do sports together.

錄音內容

M: I'm glad we **went to that meeting** yesterday.

W: Me, too. It was nice being able to say how we feel about things.

M: Yeah. **Our manager** is so great. I wouldn't trade him for Susan in Sales.

W: I agree. She has a reputation for being **hard to work for**.

解析

- 從兩人談話內容的關鍵字詞如「去開會」、「我們的經理」、「難以共事」等可知兩人關係為同事，故答案選 (C)。

🎧 Track 63

Exercise

Listen to the audio track. Answer the following question about what the speakers say in each conversation.

Conversation 1

Q: What is the man and woman's relationship?
(A) Coworkers
(B) Teacher and student
(C) Husband and wife
(D) Doctor and patient
Your answer: Ⓐ Ⓑ Ⓒ Ⓓ

Conversation 2

Q: What is Jessica's job?
(A) A CEO   (B) A secretary
(C) A maintenance worker   (D) A manager
Your answer: Ⓐ Ⓑ Ⓒ Ⓓ

Part 3 Short Conversations

題型 2 與「事件」有關

常考問題	解題技巧
a. 問主題／目的： • What are the speakers (mainly) discussing? • What are the speakers (mainly) talking about? • What is the purpose of . . . ?	💡 主旨題（main idea）屬於必要把握的送分題型，因為答案常遍布於整個對話中，就算不小心聽漏了某一部分，仍有機會選出正確答案。這類題型可聽完全部對話再綜合全部資訊來作答。
b. 問意見或觀感： • How does the man/woman feel (about . . .)? • What does the man/woman think/say about . . . ? **c.** 問動作或做法： • What does sb. plan/want/hope to do? • What does the man/woman suggest the woman/man do? • What does the man/woman offer to do (for the woman/man)?	💡 問某人意見／觀感或動作／做法時，若題目是問 man，答案通常可從 man 的陳述中找出。同樣地，題目中若是問 woman，則要特別注意聽 woman 的敘述。

Example 1

🎧 Track 64

Q What are the speakers discussing?

A (A) The woman's potential new position
(B) The man's vacation to Brazil
(C) How to ask for a raise
(D) Different cultures around the world

錄音內容

W: The manager just **offered me a promotion**. I'm not sure if I should take the offer.

M: Really? Why? It comes with **better money and benefits**, right?

W: Yeah, but I'd need to **relocate abroad**. It's in Brazil.

M: Go for it! It's an **opportunity to advance**. Plus you'll get to experience a new culture.

解析

• 本題問對話主旨，由關鍵字詞：「提供升遷」、「較好的薪資和福利」、「轉調國外」及「晉升的機會」等，可知兩人在討論可能的新職務，故答案選 (A)。

Example 2

🎧 Track 65

 Q How does the **man feel about** missing the game?

 (A) Satisfied
(B) Surprised
(C) Relieved
(D) Disappointed

錄音內容

W: Did you watch the game last night?

M: I saw the score on the evening news, but I didn't see any more than that. Was it good?

W: I'd say it was the game of the year. You really missed out. Brad Kenny was amazing.

M: **Ah, what a shame. I guess I'll have to download it from somewhere.**

解析

- 問男子的感覺，故要仔細聆聽男子的敘述，由最後一句「啊，真可惜呀。我想我得去下載來看了。」可知答案選 (D)。

🎧 Track 66

Exercise

Listen to the audio track. Answer the following question about what the speakers say in each conversation.

Conversation 1

Q: What are the speakers mainly talking about?
 (A) What they deserve (B) Giving money to charity
 (C) Making money (D) Cancer
 Your answer: Ⓐ Ⓑ Ⓒ Ⓓ

Conversation 2

Q: What does the man suggest the woman do?
 (A) Go to the bank tomorrow
 (B) Use the Internet to save money
 (C) Transfer money over the Internet
 (D) Use the telephone
 Your answer: Ⓐ Ⓑ Ⓒ Ⓓ

Part 3 Short Conversations

題型 3 與「細節」有關

常考問題

a. 問時間、星期幾或日期
   例 When did the woman expect sth. to be started?

b. 問地點
   例 Where did the man/woman plan to go?

c. 問數字或多少錢
   例 How many people do the speakers expect for the conference?

d. 問方式
   例 How did the man/woman get to work this morning?

e. 問物件
   例 What does the man/woman give the woman/man?

解題技巧

相對於主旨題等類型的問題可以等到最後再答，細節題是一聽到對話中提及就要馬上作答的。務必要預先瀏覽題目及選項並猜測可能的問題點，以便從對話中找出答案。

Example 1

Track 67

Q What **day** will the speakers leave on their trip?

A (A) Monday
(B) Tuesday
(C) Wednesday
(D) Thursday

錄音內容

M: When do you want to schedule our trip to Hong Kong?

W: I'm busy next Monday and Tuesday. What about after that?

M: **How about Wednesday?** I'll be ready on Wednesday.

W: **That'll work**. Then we'll have two whole days there.

解析

• 本題問 What day「哪一天」，對話中男子說「星期三如何呢？」，而女子回應「可以啊。」可知答案選 (C)。

Example 2

Track 68

Q **How long** will it take for the **parts to come**?

A (A) Two days
(B) Two weeks
(C) Ten days
(D) Two months

錄音內容

W: So how much will it cost to fix?

M: Well, it's an old car now, so it is difficult to get **the parts**.

W: I see. If you order them, **how long** will they take to arrive?

M: We have to get them from overseas, so it could take a while. Possibly **two months** I'm afraid.

解析

- 本題問 How long . . . parts to come?「零件要多久才會來?」,答案為男子所回應的 . . . two months,故答案選 (D)。

Track 69

Exercise

Listen to the audio track. Answer the following question about what the speakers say in each conversation.

Conversation 1

Q: When will someone come to fix the air conditioner?
(A) Later today   (B) Tomorrow
(C) The end of the week (D) Next month
Your answer: Ⓐ Ⓑ Ⓒ Ⓓ

Conversation 2

Q: How much will the seats the woman suggests cost?
(A) Free of charge   (B) 10 dollars
(C) 45 dollars   (D) 70 dollars
Your answer: Ⓐ Ⓑ Ⓒ Ⓓ

Part 3 Short Conversations

題型 4 推論題

常考問題

這類題型問句中多半含以下字眼：

- most likely
- probably/might
- inferred/implied

例 Where does sb. probably work?

例 What type of company do the speakers most likely work for?

解題技巧

💡 推論型題目（inference questions）屬 Part 3 中難度較高的題型，正確答案並沒有在對話中明講。成功答題的秘訣在於聽出關鍵字詞後，能靠合理、邏輯的思考模式推敲出答案。

Example 1

🎧 Track 70

Q Where does the man probably work?

A
(A) A supermarket
(B) A modeling agency
(C) A gym
(D) A park

錄音內容

W: Hello there. This is Sally Stewart. Is Hugh Lee there by any chance?

M: Hi, Sally. I'm Dennis, Hugh's new assistant. Hugh's away on business at the moment. Can I help you with something?

W: Yes, please. I just want to make sure he got my résumé **for the fitness trainer** position. I e-mailed it yesterday.

M: OK, Sally. Let me have a look and get back to you. If I can't find it, I'll ask Hugh to contact you when he returns tomorrow.

解析

- 由女子跟男子說「我打電話來是要詢問有關健身教練（fitness trainer）的職缺。」，並問對方是否有收到履歷（résumé），可推知男子可能是在健身房工作，答案選 (C)。

Example 2

🎧 Track 71

Q What kind of company does the woman most likely work for?

A (A) A newspaper
(B) A software developer
(C) A sportswear store
(D) A finance company

錄音內容

M: Hello there. I'm calling about the **business copy editor** position. Is it still available?

W: I'm afraid that position has now been filled, but we're still hiring for positions **in the features and sports departments** if you're interested.

M: I'm definitely interested. What do I need to do?

W: Well, send us your résumé first, and if you look like a good fit, we'll call you for an interview next week.

解析

- 由對話中男子詢問女子關於該公司「商業版編輯」的職缺，及女子回應「專題及運動部門」還有在徵人，可推知她的公司是與「報紙」相關的行業，故答案選 (A)。

🎧 Track 72

Exercise

Listen to the audio track. Answer the following question about what the speakers say in each conversation.

Conversation 1

Q: Where is this conversation most likely taking place?
(A) In a shopping mall   (B) In a hospital
(C) In a train station   (D) In a fitness center
Your answer: Ⓐ Ⓑ Ⓒ Ⓓ

Conversation 2

Q: What does the woman imply about the person she will meet?
(A) He is very tall.   (B) He works for the government.
(C) He wants to offer her a job. (D) He can afford to make a large order.
Your answer: Ⓐ Ⓑ Ⓒ Ⓓ

Part 3 Short Conversations

題型 5 考口語用法或句意

常考問題	解題技巧
• Why does the woman/man say, ". . ."? • What does the woman/man mean when she/he says, ". . ."?	💡 先瀏覽題目看是要詢問男子或女子所說，然後聽對話時仔細聆聽該句出現的地方並根據上下文推斷出語意。

Example 1
🎧 Track 73

Q What does the first man mean when he says, "that'll do it"?

A
(A) They have finished dinner.
(B) They are ready to pay.
(C) Neither of them will drink coffee.
(D) They will look at the dessert menu

W: Hi gentlemen. I see you've finished. Is here anything else I can get you for now, maybe a look at the dessert menu and a coffee, or just the check?
MA: I think **that'll do it** for us. We've got a meeting to rush off to.
MB: Actually, I wouldn't mind a cup of joe. Can I take one to go?
W: We do have cups for takeout. I'll add it to the bill. It should only take a moment.
MA: Now that you mention it, I may as well have one, too. We still haven't finished those reports. It's going to be a long afternoon, and I could use the pick-me-up.
W: I know the feeling. Let me get your coffee and I'll bring your bill right out. Cream and sugar?
MB: No, just black for me.
MA: Me too. Do you have the client's office address? We can't be late.
MB: It's in the car, with the presentation.

解析
• **that'll do it** 為口語用法，常用在不需要其他任何東西時，指「那樣就行了」。由對話中上一句女子詢問要點甜點、咖啡或是結帳，以及男子 A 回應說「我們還要趕去一場會議。」可以推測男子 A 說 **that'll do it** 是指不用再點甜點或咖啡，而要馬上結帳之意，故正確答案為 (B)。

Example 2

🎧 Track 74

 Q What does Darien most likely mean when he says "trim the fat"?

 A (A) Increase income by collecting more on penalties
(B) Get rid of penalties and expenses completely
(C) Reduce overall penalties and expenses
(D) Illegally avoid paying penalties and expenses

W: Darien, it's nice to meet you. Please, have a seat.
MA: Thank you. Oh, and this is Andrew, my personal intern.
MB: Nice to meet you, ma'am. Thank you for taking this meeting with us.
W: A pleasure to meet you as well. Now, what did you want to discuss?
MA: Well, we would like to talk about possibly handling your taxes for you. We could do an excellent job and likely save you some money.
W: Is that so?
MA: Yes, ma'am. We believe that there are several areas where we can **trim the fat** regarding penalties and expenditures.
W: I'm listening. What do you have in mind?
MB: Here is a rough plan of what we could do for you.

解析

- 本題問「Darien 說 trim the fat 是什麼意思？」。trim the fat 字面原指「削減脂肪；減重」，口語中亦常用來指「縮減掉多餘或不必要的事物」。由上面一句 Darien 對女子說「我們可以做得很好，而且很可能可以幫您省下一些錢。」並進一步向女子說明可以為其減少罰金和支出額，因此答案選 (C)。

🎧 Track 75

Exercise

Listen to the audio track. Answer the following question about what the speakers say in the conversation.

Q: Why does the woman say, "get back to us soon"?
(A) She wants the man to return to the office.
(B) She believes that the man will reply to the e-mail Robert sent.
(C) She expects the man to call when he arrives at the office.
(D) She thinks the man is lost.

Your answer: Ⓐ Ⓑ Ⓒ Ⓓ

題型 6 　圖表題

常考問題	解題技巧
• Look at the graphic. Wh- question . . . ? • Based on the graphic and the conversation, wh- question . . . ?	考生應試時須一心二用，耳朵在聽對話的同時，眼睛要同時閱讀圖表的資訊內容。看到題目後先快速瀏覽圖表及相關問題，然後答題時整合對話內容及圖表所呈現的資訊來作答。

Example 1

Track 76

Q Look at the graphic. What size light would best suit the speakers' needs?

Light Size (watts) and Price

$100　　　　$150　　　　$200　　　　$350

A (A) 100w　　(B) 150w　　(C) 300w　　(D) 600w

W: We need to get some new lights for our greenhouse. These vegetables aren't going to grow themselves!
M: Yeah, I know. I've been reading up on different light sizes.
W: Well, I don't think we need a very big one—we don't grow that much produce. **The smallest size will do**.
M: True, I don't know the price though. I need to look at the website.
W: Once you do that, I can go to the store and buy it. I don't want to buy it online with a credit card.
M: Sounds good. I'll take a look at the prices and let you know.

解析

• 本題詢問圖表中哪一種燈最符合說話者的需求。由對話中女子說 The smallest size will do.「最小尺寸的就足夠了」，對照圖表，其中最小尺寸的燈泡為 150w，故答案選 (B)。

Example 2

🎧 Track 77

Q Look at the graphic. What drink will the man order with his burger?

Cheeseburger	$8	Beer	$5
Hotdog	$7	Soda	$3
Nachos	$5	Water	$2
Juice	$6		

A (A) Beer (B) Soda (C) Water (D) Juice

W: So, what would you like to order?

M: Hmm, well, it all looks so good . . . and I am very hungry, but—plus the tickets—the company only gave us a $20 stipend to split. I am going to have to choose wisely.

W: I'm going to get what I always get when I watch a game at the stadium—nachos and a beer.

M: Well, I really want a burger . . . But how much does that leave me with for a drink?

W: Not much.

M: Ah, you're right. Well that's fair at least. **My food and drink will add up to ten bucks**, and so will yours.

> 解析
>
> - 本題詢問男子會點什麼飲料搭配漢堡。對話最後男子提到 My food and drink will add up to ten bucks「我的食物和飲料加起來十美元」。而根據圖表漢堡是八美元，因此男子飲料只能選擇二美元的水，故正確答案為 (C)。

🎧 Track 78

Exercise

Listen to the audio track. Answer the following question about what the speakers say in the conversation.

Q: Look at the graphic and consider the dialogue. What action will Tom take?
(A) He will put on the chemicals away into storage.
(B) He will mark one of the chemicals on the list.
(C) He will request a fifth chemical.
(D) He will mix some chemicals.

Your answer: Ⓐ Ⓑ Ⓒ Ⓓ

Chemical	Amount(g)
Heptane	1200g
Hexane	926g
Phosphorous	10000g
Potassium	1000g

Part 3 Short Conversations

Practice Test PART 3

Directions:
You will hear some conversations between two or more people. You will be asked to answer three questions about what the speakers say in each conversation. Select the best response to each question and mark the letter (A), (B), (C), or (D) on your answer sheet. The conversations will not be printed in your test book and will be spoken only one time.

🎧 Track 79

1. What are they moving?
   - (A) Kitchenware
   - (B) Sports equipment
   - (C) A car
   - (D) Office equipment

2. Where are they taking it?
   - (A) Alan's office
   - (B) To another room
   - (C) To the next floor
   - (D) Downstairs

3. Who will the woman ask for help?
   - (A) Dave
   - (B) Alan
   - (C) Carl
   - (D) Helen

4. What is the man and woman's relationship?
   - (A) They are coworkers.
   - (B) They are spouses.
   - (C) They are classmates.
   - (D) They are neighbors.

5. Why can't the man cook dinner today?
   - (A) He can't cook very well.
   - (B) He has a dentist's appointment.
   - (C) He has to stay late for a meeting.
   - (D) He is meeting a friend after work.

6. What does the woman suggest they do?
   - (A) Eat separately
   - (B) Eat in a fancy restaurant
   - (C) Cook dinner together
   - (D) Get food to take home

7. How did the man know about the new sales plan?
   (A) The woman spoke to him about it before.
   (B) He heard about it from their coworker.
   (C) The woman e-mailed it to him.
   (D) It came up in a meeting before.

8. Who is Phil most likely to be?
   (A) The man and woman's boss
   (B) A friend of the woman's
   (C) The man and woman's employee
   (D) The delivery man

9. What is the woman going to do at the meeting?
   (A) Avoid talking to Phil
   (B) Talk about the new plan
   (C) Arrange a separate meeting with Phil
   (D) Think of a new plan

10. What is the occupation of both speakers?
    (A) They're engineers.
    (B) They work in entertainment.
    (C) They work for a charity.
    (D) They're students.

11. What is the woman planning to do?
    (A) Help with an aid project
    (B) Give money to a charitable organization
    (C) Take a video of a water treatment plant
    (D) Give lectures on the status of Africa

12. What would her responsibilities be?
    (A) Paying her loan
    (B) Training and building
    (C) Managing the facility
    (D) Raising money and treating patients

13. What are the speakers mainly talking about?
    (A) The place they are visiting with their tour group
    (B) The sights they have enjoyed the most on the tour
    (C) Their opinions about traveling with a group
    (D) The most convenient methods of traveling

14. How does the man feel about their vacation?
    (A) He's having an excellent time on the trip.
    (B) He isn't sure about the places they're seeing.
    (C) He isn't really enjoying the weather.
    (D) He would like to have more freedom.

15. What does the woman think about traveling alone?
    (A) It's more convenient than joining a group.
    (B) It's boring because you have no one to talk to.
    (C) It's not as easy as traveling in a group.
    (D) It's not safe for women to travel alone.

16. What is the couple talking about?
    (A) The local geography
    (B) Plans for their time off
    (C) What they plan to buy
    (D) How they plan to travel

17. What does the man say about the mall?
    (A) They won't need to spend much time there.
    (B) They should go there every day of the long weekend.
    (C) He doesn't want to go.
    (D) It will be closed the whole weekend.

18. What do we know about the weather?
    (A) It's going to be snowy this weekend.
    (B) It has been cold and rainy recently.
    (C) It is constantly changing.
    (D) It has been nice for the last few days.

19. Who are most likely the speakers in the conversation?
    (A) Professors
    (B) Receptionists
    (C) Interns
    (D) Managers

20. What does the woman mean when she says "let Harrison go"?
    (A) Terminate his employment
    (B) Send him home early
    (C) Dismiss him from the meeting
    (D) Have him go on a business trip

21. What was a previous issue with Harrison?
    (A) He was often late to work.
    (B) He didn't find a replacement.
    (C) He changed his behavior too often.
    (D) He worked too much overtime.

22. What are they mainly talking about?
    (A) Buying another company
    (B) Selling their company
    (C) Selling in Asia
    (D) Stocks

23. Where might this conversation be taking place?
    (A) In a restroom
    (B) In a boardroom
    (C) In a kitchen
    (D) In a living room

24. How does the woman feel about the deal after talking to the man?
    (A) She thinks it's a bad idea.
    (B) She agrees with what he says.
    (C) She is hesitant about making any changes.
    (D) She's unsure if the man is telling the truth.

Part 3 Short Conversations

25. How does Jane feel?
    (A) Angry
    (B) Sad
    (C) Sick
    (D) Stressed

26. Which of these is NOT a change in Jane's life?
    (A) Working at a new place
    (B) Moving house
    (C) Death of her mother
    (D) Birth of a new baby

27. Who might Mark be?
    (A) Jane's coworker
    (B) Jane's friend
    (C) Jane's boss
    (D) Jane's husband

28. What is this conversation mainly about?
    (A) A call-in radio contest
    (B) An event at a beach
    (C) Family trips
    (D) Styles of music

29. Why does the second male speaker say "that's a piece of cake" in response to the woman?
    (A) Anyone can participate in the competition.
    (B) He thinks she should have known.
    (C) It is an easy question to answer.
    (D) It is the answer to the question.

30. Why doesn't the first man want to take the music festival tickets?
    (A) He doesn't like music.
    (B) He is going to the beach with his family.
    (C) The concert is too far away.
    (D) There are too many people at music festivals.

31. What does the woman say about the courses?
    (A) They are very popular.
    (B) They aren't very interesting.
    (C) They are expensive.
    (D) They require previous experience.

32. Look at the graphic. How much will the man's course cost?
    (A) $150
    (B) $185
    (C) $215
    (D) $245

Colitory – The Interchange of Digital Learning

Spaces available in the following courses

Capturing Black and White Photography
Instructor: Mario Lupez $185

Coloring the Photos of Yesterday
Instructor: Janeane Harpo $245

Video Production Techniques
Instructor: Karl Saget $215

33. What does the woman say about the course Ken is interested in?
    (A) It is sold out.
    (B) It lasts for six weeks.
    (C) There are spots available.
    (D) He must pay the course fee in cash.

34. What is the relationship between the speakers?
    (A) They are coworkers.
    (B) The woman is the man's boss.
    (C) The man is the woman's customer.
    (D) They are Mike's parents.

35. When will the man collect his car?
    (A) Right away
    (B) After lunch
    (C) In two days
    (D) After work

Customer Names	Status
1. Laura Nader	Finished, picking up on Friday
2. Brett McKenzie	Hydraulic line arriving today
3. Beverly D'Antonio	Tail light panel arriving today or tomorrow
4. Reggie Price	Call back with estimate today

36. Look at the graphic. What delayed the speakers?
    (A) A hydraulic line wasn't immediately available.
    (B) A tail light panel wasn't immediately available.
    (C) An estimate had not yet been completed.
    (D) A person couldn't come sooner for a pickup.

Part 3 Short Conversations

Don't Fear the Cheddar $10
(Ham, Cheddar, Wheat Toast)

Sweet Home Italy $15
(Spaghetti, Meatballs, Parmesan)

More Than a Mushroom $14
(Mushroom, Swiss, Beef Patty, Bun)

Fish over Troubled Water $15
(Fish, Veggies, Taco Shell)

That's Amore $13
(Caesar salad)

(w/ chicken +$4) (w/ salmon + $7)

Blitzkrieg Beef $17
(Roast beef, grilled vegetables)

37. Which is NOT a concern the woman has regarding her order?
    (A) Whether the food is fresh
    (B) The ingredients
    (C) How long it will take to prepare
    (D) Accepted payment methods

38. What is the most likely reason that the woman changed her order?
    (A) She doesn't have enough time.
    (B) She is allergic to that menu item.
    (C) She doesn't have enough money.
    (D) She changed her mind about what she wanted.

39. Look at the graphic. Which item could the woman NOT eat?
    (A) Fish over Troubled Water
    (B) Blitzkrieg Beef
    (C) That's Amore
    (D) Sweet Home Italy

Part 4　Short Talks 簡短獨白

題型介紹

題數	三十題（多益考試兩百題中的第 71~100 題）
題型說明	• 會聽到 10 組不同類型的一人獨白（常見獨白類型請見 p.70）。 • 每組獨白各有三個問題，10 組獨白共 30 題。 • 每題組的<u>問題和答案選項都出現在題本中</u>。
題目時間間隔	約 7~8 秒
題目範例	🎧 Track 80 1. What is the purpose of this talk? 　(A) To announce the winner of an award 　(B) To entertain young people 　(C) To introduce a guest speaker 　(D) To explain a problem 2. What field does Francis Butcher work in? 　(A) Entertainment 　(B) Charity 　(C) Exercise 　(D) Education 3. What does the speaker think is hard? 　(A) Getting children to listen 　(B) Getting children to exercise 　(C) Getting children to write 　(D) Getting children to eat vegetables 正解 1.(C) 2.(A) 3.(B)

基本作答流程與技巧

Step 1　瀏覽題目及選項

利用一開始播放 Direction 的時間瀏覽第一個題組的題目及選項，並判斷獨白可能的主題及方向。

Step 2　仔細聽介紹句

每一題組的介紹句 "Questions . . . to . . . refer to the following (talk type)." 會有助於進一步幫助你正確判斷主題和獨白情境。

Step 3　掌握問題點及作答順序

題組答題順序有七八成會依照順序問，一般來說可依序作答（如 p.46 小提醒所提，先做記號即可），但概念同 Part 3，與整體內容相關的「主旨題」可最後作答，細節題則要馬上作答。

Step 4　預覽下一道題組

在各題組第三道題目唸完的同時，完成該題組的作答（記得將之前僅做記號答案填滿）。然後利用與下一題組間的 7~8 秒時間，瀏覽下一個題組的題目及選項。

Part 4 Short Talks

常考題型

	題型	常考問題	解題技巧
與獨白整體內容相關	1. 問主旨或目的	• What is the message/talk mainly about? • What is the (main) topic of . . . ? • What is the (main) purpose of . . . ?	屬必考題型，30 題中大約會出 3~4 題。通常可由獨白內容中多處地方聽出整體訊息並做判斷。
	2. 問說話者的身份	• Who is the speaker? • Who (most likely) is sb.? • What is sb.'s position/job/occupation?	問說話者本身是誰，或是問獨白中所提到之某人的身份或職業等，要注意聽人名、人物相關工作的描述等訊息。
	3. 問談話的對象	• Who is being addressed? • Who is the audience for this talk? • Who is the intended audience for this talk/announcement? • Who (most likely) are the listeners?	問這段獨白的主要對象是誰，通常須由整體內容和訊息的性質來判斷。
與獨白部分內容相關	4. 細節題	常見問題包括： • 人名，例 Who will do sth.? • 時間或日期，例 What time . . . ? / When . . . ? • 地點，例 Where is . . . located? • 天氣，例 How is the weather. . . ? / What is the highest/lowest temperature expected . . . ? • 物品，例 What does . . . sell?	如同 Part 3，在 Part 4「簡短獨白」中，這類問題的答案選項同樣會比較短，一定要先預覽題目和選項，然後針對題目一聽到答案便即刻作答。

	題型	常考問題	📝 解題技巧
與獨白部分內容相關	5. 問事件內容、原因或行動	• What does the speaker say about / want . . . ? • What problem does sb. mention? • What will sb. do? • Why . . . ?	💡 這類問題問法比較沒有固定模式。務必事先瀏覽題目及選項以便聽獨白時抓出解題的關鍵字句。
	6. 題目含 will . . . next/ last 字眼的題型	• What will happen last/next? • What will the speaker/listeners (most likely) do next? • What will the next talk be about?	💡 問何事會最後或緊接著發生，或是問接下來的談話內容為何。這類題型的答案常會在獨白的<u>後段</u>出現。
	7. 問口語用法或句意	• What does the speaker mean/ imply when he/she says, ". . ."? • What does the speaker mean/ imply by saying . . . ? • Why does the speaker say, ". . ."?	💡 須仔細聆聽該句於獨白中何時出現，並依上下文來判斷其含意。
高難度題型（常須整合全部內容）	8. 是非題／除外題	• What is true about . . . ? • What is NOT (true about) . . . ? • Which of the following . . . NOT . . . ?	💡 須仔細閱讀所有選項並找出關鍵字詞，然後整合所有聽到的資訊才能篩選出答案。這類問題建議可聽完整段獨白後最後再作答。
	9. 推論題	• What does the speaker imply about . . . ? • What is implied about . . . ?	💡 題目中看到 infer / imply / might / most likely 等字眼即為推論題。須由獨白中的相關訊息去推敲出合理答案。
	10. 圖表題	• Look at the graphic. Wh- question . . . ? • Based on the graphic and the talk, wh- question . . . ?	💡 須整合獨白訊息及圖表資訊來答題。要注意圖表所呈現的不代表就是最後的正確資訊，有時獨白中會另外說明有變更或異動等。

獨白類型與常考問題

獨白類型	題材	常考問題點
Announcement 公告或宣布	★ 機場或機艙廣播 ★ 商場或公共場所廣播 ★ 辦公室公告	• 公告的對象（題型 3） • 公告的可能地點（題型 9） • 公告的目的（題型 1） • 公告及圖表（題型 10）
Introduction 介紹或引言	★ 介紹來賓 ★ 公司或產品簡介 ★ 會議或活動開場白 ★ 導覽介紹	• 來賓的身份及專業領域（題型 2） • 可能的聽眾群（題型 3） • 活動的目的（題型 1） • 下一步將會做什麼（題型 6）
Media Broadcast 廣播或電視媒體	★ 電視或電台節目 ★ 新聞報導 ★ 廣告行銷 ★ 路況或天氣報導	• 節目播出時間（題型 4） • 節目宗旨（題型 1） • 廣告產品可能的類別（題型 9） • 某天或某時的天氣狀況（題型 4）
Voice Message 語音訊息	★ 電話留言 ★ 電話語音系統	• 留言的主要原因（題型 1） • 說話者希望對方有何做法或回應（題型 5） • 語音系統內的指示或步驟（題型 5） • 問口語用法或句意（題型 7）
Speech/Lecture 演講	★ 各類主題演講 ★ 會議簡報 ★ 得獎感言 ★ 退休感言	• 講者的身份（題型 2） • 可能的聽眾群（題型 3） • 演講主要題材及內容（題型 1）

得分秘技：想像力的培養

Part 4 獨白內容較長且整段僅由一人說明，難免較為乏味。一連十個題組聽下來，很容易會在中途分心，或是抓不到重點。

故在此運用「想像力」並採用「圖像聯想法」，可增加自己對獨白的注意力及記憶力，進而有助於正確答題。

想像自己就是獨白的說話對象（例如：若是導覽說明，就想像自己是參觀者或遊客；而獨白在一場公司餐會中，則想像自己是該公司員工），在腦海中描繪影像並融入劇情中。以下為如何運用想像力的範例：

Questions 1 through 3 refer to the following announcement.

➡ 聽介紹句得知獨白為某種宣布事項

🎧 Track 81

Settle down everyone. Please take your assigned seats on the **bus** now. Thank you.

➡ 想像自己坐在巴士內

On our trip today, we will be visiting the **zoo** and the **botanical gardens**.

➡ 想像將會參觀動物園和植物園

We should arrive at the zoo at around **ten o'clock**.

➡ 想像時鐘上的時間為十點

When we're in the zoo, **do not give the animals any food**.

➡ 想像禁止餵食的警告標示

At **one o'clock** we'll be getting back on the bus to go to the botanical gardens.

➡ 想像一點回到巴士上並前往植物園

First, we'll **eat lunch**, and then we'll take a **look at the beautiful flowers and trees**.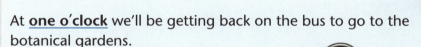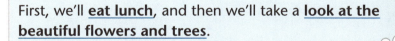

➡ 想像吃午餐及參觀花草樹木

We'll be getting back on the bus once more at **three o'clock**.

➡ 想像三點又回到巴士上

While we're on the bus, there will be **no eating or drinking**. Please **keep your voices low** and stay in your seats at all times.

➡ 想像車上禁止飲食並要輕聲細語

Part 4 簡短獨白

Part 4 Short Talks

獨白類型 1 Announcement 公告或宣布

Example

🎧 Track 82

1. Where might we hear this announcement?
   (A) On a train
   (B) In an airport
   (C) In a train station
   (D) On a bus

2. Why did something need to be changed?
   (A) The platform closes early on weekdays.
   (B) A problem happened with an earlier train.
   (C) The train can not go directly to the destination.
   (D) The train is supposed to arrive early.

3. Look at the graphic. What time will the train bound for Jersey City leave?
   (A) 2:15
   (B) 2:20
   (C) 2:25
   (D) 2:30

📝 **解題技巧**

Step 1

瀏覽題目和選項，由關鍵字詞 train、airport、bus、platform、destination 等推測獨白內容可能與搭乘大眾運輸有關。

Step 2

找出問題點：
① 公告或宣布的地點
② 變更的原因
③ 問火車離站時間

Next train to	Platform	Scheduled for	Status
Clifton Heights	11	02:30 p.m.	On time
Jersey City	19	02:15 p.m.	On time
Morton	04	Please ask staff	
Rehoboth Beach	26	03:35 p.m.	On time
Scranton	09	02:25 p.m.	On time
Wheeling	29	04:10 p.m.	Delayed
Wilkes-Barre	14	02:10 p.m.	On time

錄音內容

Questions 1 through 3 refer to the following announcement and schedule.

This is an announcement for all **passengers who are traveling to Jersey City**.

All passengers must go to platform 27 instead of the previously announced platform 19 **because of an earlier delayed train** from Scranton.

There will also be a five minute delay due to the platform change. Network Rail apologizes for any inconvenience caused, and we hope that you have a pleasant journey.

解析

Q1 問獨白可能的地點，須由相關訊息推斷，可最後再作答。首句即說明公告對象為搭乘前往澤西市的旅客，且由後面內容中得知宣布要更換月台，故可知地點應該是在 (C) 火車站。

Q2 問造成變更的原因。關鍵詞 because of... 後即為答案，故選 (B)「稍早的火車發生問題」。

Q3 為圖表題，搭配題目上的表格得知到澤西市火車預計下午兩點十五分離駛，而廣播中聽到 There will also be a five minute delay due to the platform change. 故得知答案為 (B)。

🎧 *Track 83*

Exercise

Listen to the audio track. Answer the three questions about what the speaker says in the talk.

1. Where does the speaker most likely work?
   (A) A machine shop
   (B) A laboratory
   (C) A software company
   (D) A financial institution
   Your answer: Ⓐ Ⓑ Ⓒ Ⓓ

2. What were the employees instructed to do with the parts they did not order?
   (A) Keep them on hand
   (B) Dispose of them
   (C) Return them
   (D) List them for sale
   Your answer: Ⓐ Ⓑ Ⓒ Ⓓ

3. Look at the graphic. How many sprockets arrived?
   (A) Zero   (B) Forty-eight   (C) Fifty   (D) Fifty-two
   Your answer: Ⓐ Ⓑ Ⓒ Ⓓ

Part Type	Quantity
Helical Gear	50
Camshaft	22
Alternator	14
Sprocket	50
Piston	8

Part 4 簡短獨白

Part 4　Short Talks

獨白類型 2　Introduction　介紹或引言

Example
🎧 Track 84

1. Who is the intended audience for this talk?
   (A) Students
   (B) New employees
   (C) Tourists
   (D) New clients

2. How long will the program last?
   (A) One week
   (B) Five days
   (C) Two weeks
   (D) Ten days

3. What is something that will be taught?
   (A) How to sell computer programs
   (B) How to pay attention to clients
   (C) How to find new clients
   (D) How to repair computers

解題技巧

Step 1
瀏覽題目和選項，由關鍵字詞 program、be taught 等推測獨白內容可能與某種課程有關。

Step 2
找出問題點：
① 談話的對象
② 課程為期多長時間
③ 教導的內容

錄音內容

Questions 1 through 3 refer to the following talk.

Hi, and welcome to our company and our company's **training program**.

This **two-week program** will teach you all about our company and your jobs as sales representatives. **As new staff**, you'll learn a lot.

解析

Q1 問獨白談話的對象。由首句提到 training program「訓練課程」及後面說明 As new staff「新進員工」將會學習到的事項，可知答案選 (B)。

Q2 為細節題，聽到第二句 two-week program 即知答案選 (C)。

We have a very special sales approach that makes sure each sales representative **pays special attention to his or her clients**. **Paying attention to clients** is what has made our company successful. During these two weeks, you'll also be learning how to use our company's computer software. Now, let's get started.

Q3 問課程教導的內容。由獨白中關鍵字詞 pays special attention to . . . clients 可知答案選 (B)。其他選項可用刪去法再次確認並非課程教授的內容。

🎧 Track 85

Exercise

Listen to the audio track. Answer the three questions about what the speaker says in the talk.

1. What kind of event is this?
   (A) A factory tour
   (B) A history lecture
   (C) A shopping activity
   (D) A cooking class
   Your answer: Ⓐ Ⓑ Ⓒ Ⓓ

2. What has happened to St. Algernon's Cheese Works over the years?
   (A) It has gotten smaller.
   (B) It has started making other products.
   (C) It has increased in size.
   (D) It has moved locations several times.
   Your answer: Ⓐ Ⓑ Ⓒ Ⓓ

3. What will happen last?
   (A) The group will visit the production floor.
   (B) The group will taste and buy some cheese.
   (C) The group will learn how to start a business.
   (D) The group will meet the cheese makers.
   Your answer: Ⓐ Ⓑ Ⓒ Ⓓ

Part 4　Short Talks

獨白類型 3　Media Broadcast　廣播或電視媒體

Example
🎧 Track 86

1. What is the weather like today?
   (A) It is warm.
   (B) It is hot.
   (C) It is snowy.
   (D) It is cold.

2. When will the weather warm up?
   (A) On Tuesday
   (B) On Thursday
   (C) Tomorrow
   (D) Today

3. When will inland temperatures reach 100 degrees?
   (A) Tomorrow
   (B) Thursday
   (C) Friday
   (D) Saturday

📝 解題技巧

Step 1

瀏覽題目和選項，由關鍵字詞 weather、warm up、temperature 等推測獨白內容可能與天氣報導有關。

Step 2

找出問題點：
① 今天的天氣
② 天氣何時變暖
③ 內陸何時達到一百度

錄音內容

Questions 1 through 3 refer to the following weather forecast.

And now it is time for our five-day weather forecast. It looks like it is going to be **cold again tomorrow, just like today**, with highs in the 50s along the coast and in the 60s inland.

And we'll likely have more rain tomorrow, too. **But on Thursday**, the day after tomorrow, **it is going to begin warming up**. On Thursday, we can expect clear skies, with highs in the 70s along the coast and the 80s inland.

解析

聽介紹句確認獨白內容為天氣預報。

Q1 問今天的天氣。由句中關鍵字詞 . . . cold again tomorrow, just like today . . .「明天天氣會和今天一樣冷」可知答案選 (D)。

Q2 為細節題，問天氣何時會變暖。關鍵字詞為 But on Thursday . . . warming up 可知答案選 (B)。請注意，聽到對話中有轉折詞（如在此的 but）時，往往要特別留心聽其後敘述的內容。

| **Then on Saturday and Sunday**, we'll see even hotter temperatures, with highs in the 80s along the coast and **temperatures above 100 degrees inland**. | **Q3** 為細節題，問內陸何時達到華氏一百度。預先瀏覽題目即知聽獨白時要專注於 inland、100 degrees 等字詞，文中提到是在週六及週日，故相符的答案為 (D)。 |

🎧 *Track 87*

Exercise

Listen to the audio track. Answer the three questions about what the speaker says in the talk.

1. What is the purpose of this ad?
   (A) To sell computers
   (B) To get new students
   (C) To raise money for a school
   (D) To attract good teachers
   Your answer: Ⓐ Ⓑ Ⓒ Ⓓ

2. What kind of training does the college offer?
   (A) Nursing
   (B) Art
   (C) Computer skills
   (D) Teaching skills
   Your answer: Ⓐ Ⓑ Ⓒ Ⓓ

3. According to the commercial, which industry is constantly hiring?
   (A) Health care
   (B) Education
   (C) Technology
   (D) Clean energy
   Your answer: Ⓐ Ⓑ Ⓒ Ⓓ

Part 4 Short Talks

獨白類型 4 Voice Message 語音訊息

Example
🎧 Track 88

1. What is the main purpose of this message?
   (A) To inform someone of a new rule
   (B) To make an appointment
   (C) To confirm some information
   (D) To change the date of a meeting

2. What does the speaker mean by saying "just to check in"?
   (A) He wants to get a receipt from a previous transaction.
   (B) He wants to communicate and update the status of their business relationship.
   (C) He wants to return something that is the property of the other company.
   (D) He wants to officially confirm his arrival at a certain place.

3. What does Jake want to do while they are together?
   (A) View a computer presentation
   (B) Go for a walk
   (C) Have something to eat
   (D) Tell her his problems

📝 解題技巧

Step 1

瀏覽題目和選項，由關鍵字詞 message 得知為某種訊息，而其中有人名 Jake 和 Karen，故須注意相關訊息與人物間的關係。

Step 2

找出問題點：
① 訊息主要目的
② 問句意
③ 會面時做什麼

錄音內容

Questions 1 through 3 refer to the following voice-mail message.

Hi, Karen. This is Jake. I'm going to be in town next week, and **I'm hoping I can meet with you**.

解析

聽介紹句確認獨白內容為電話語音訊息。

Q1 為主旨題。電話語音訊息中一開始往往就會說明留言的主要原因，由句中關鍵字詞 . . . I'm hoping I can meet with you.「希望能跟你見個面」可知答案選 (B)。

I am hoping to visit all of our company's clients in your area, including you, **just to check in** and see if you are happy with our company.

If you're free on Tuesday or Wednesday, I'd love to **take you out to lunch**, and we can discuss business. Please let me know if you're free on one of those days. I look forward to seeing you.

Q2 問口語用法，check in 在此有 contact、get in touch with 之意，文中即指「聯絡、聯繫一下」。後方接著說 see if you are happy with our company.「看看你對我們公司是否感到滿意。」可知答案選 (B)。

Q3 問會面時做什麼。留言者（即 Jake）提到 . . . take you out to lunch，故答案選 (C)。

🎧 Track 89

Exercise

Listen to the audio track. Answer the three questions about what the speaker says in the talk.

1. What is this message mainly about?
   (A) What kinds of people AutoFix wants to hire
   (B) How to get in touch with AutoFix
   (C) What to do if your car won't start
   (D) How much AutoFix charges for repairs
   Your answer: Ⓐ Ⓑ Ⓒ Ⓓ

2. Which is NOT mentioned as a way to contact AutoFix?
   (A) Leaving a message over the phone
   (B) Sending them an e-mail
   (C) Sending a text message
   (D) Calling back another time
   Your answer: Ⓐ Ⓑ Ⓒ Ⓓ

3. What does the speaker mean when he says, "we'll get back to you"?
   (A) There is another customer he needs to see first.
   (B) The appointment will be confirmed by e-mail.
   (C) He will return the car to the customer.
   (D) Someone will respond to the customerwe'lls message.
   Your answer: Ⓐ Ⓑ Ⓒ Ⓓ

Part 4 Short Talks

獨白類型 5 Speech/Lecture 演講

Example
🎧 Track 90

1. What is the speaker's current position?
   (A) He is a volunteer at the library.
   (B) He is a chef who cooks for large events.
   (C) He is the leader of a project.
   (D) He is a bakery manager.

2. What is the main purpose of this event?
   (A) To congratulate a local author
   (B) To show off the new library
   (C) To get volunteers
   (D) To raise money

3. Who provided the food for the dinner?
   (A) The local government
   (B) Mrs. Crane
   (C) Mr. Matthews
   (D) Mr. Pearson

📝 解題技巧

Step 1
瀏覽題目和選項，由關鍵字詞 current position、event、provided the food 得知為某項活動，且須注意說話者的身份。

Step 2
找出問題點：
① 說話者目前的職位
② 活動的主要目的
③ 由誰提供食物

【錄音內容】

Questions 1 through 3 refer to the following speech.

Hello, everybody! My name is Vernon Matthews, **chair of the Modern Library Project**, and I'd like to thank you all for coming to our third annual **fundraising dinner**.

As you all know, finding funding to keep our community library up-to-date has been getting more and more difficult over the past few years. Public funding has dropped off due to local government art cuts, so I'd like to thank everyone who has donated

【解析】

聽介紹句確認獨白內容為某種演講。

Q1 問說話者目前的職位。由一開頭講者自我介紹名字後，接著便說出職稱為 chair of . . . 故知答案選 (C)。

Q2 問活動的主要目的。由關鍵字詞 fundraising dinner「募款晚餐會」可知答案選 (D)。

their time or money to the Modern Library Project. I'd especially like to thank **Mr. Pearson for doing the catering today** and Mrs. Crane for organizing the bake sale last month. This dinner puts us closer to our target than ever. Thanks for your support!	**Q3** 為細節題，問此晚餐會是由誰提供食物。針對選項的名字或對象仔細聆聽相關訊息，由關鍵字詞 Mr. Pearson . . . catering 得知答案選 (D)。catering 指「提供飲食及服務」。

🎧 *Track 91*

Exercise

Listen to the audio track. Answer the three questions about what the speaker says in the talk.

1. What is the talk mainly about?
   (A) Celebrity gossip
   (B) The development of digital TV
   (C) How news is changing
   (D) Ms. Whitefield's career
   Your answer: Ⓐ Ⓑ Ⓒ Ⓓ

2. What is happening because of the increased number of TV channels?
   (A) Customers have more choices.
   (B) Customers have become very picky.
   (C) There is less gossip.
   (D) There is only factual news.
   Your answer: Ⓐ Ⓑ Ⓒ Ⓓ

3. How does Ms. Whitefield feel about news?
   (A) She thinks it's important to be exposed to gossip.
   (B) People should get their information from sources other than TV.
   (C) She prefers to watch only factual news.
   (D) She always follows what celebrities are doing.
   Your answer: Ⓐ Ⓑ Ⓒ Ⓓ

Part 4 Short Talks

Practice Test PART 4

Directions:
You will hear some talks given by a single speaker. You will be asked to answer three questions about what the speakers say in each talk. Select the best response to each question and mark the letter (A), (B), (C), or (D) on your answer sheet. The talks will not be printed in your test book and will be spoken only one time.

🎧 *Track 92*

1. What time will the store close?
   (A) 8:05 p.m.
   (B) 8:30 p.m.
   (C) 8:35 p.m.
   (D) 8:50 p.m.

2. Which of the following is most likely to be discounted?
   (A) A fruit salad
   (B) A bottle of cleaning solution
   (C) A carton of frozen ice cream
   (D) A magazine

3. What will close in five minutes?
   (A) The car park
   (B) The café
   (C) The whole store
   (D) The fresh food section

4. What is the weather going to be like on Friday?
   (A) Cold
   (B) Warm
   (C) Rainy
   (D) Mixed

5. Which of these temperatures is likely on Saturday during the day?
   (A) 21 degrees
   (B) 31 degrees
   (C) 35 degrees
   (D) 29 degrees

6. What is the forecast for Sunday?
   (A) Rain and low temperatures all day
   (B) Rain after 10 a.m.
   (C) Rain followed by hot weather
   (D) Rain until 10 p.m.

7. What does Denise want Stanley to do?
    (A) Buy her a new computer
    (B) Help her buy a new computer
    (C) Fix her computer
    (D) Train her to use her computer

8. Why is Denise's problem urgent?
    (A) She is selling the computer tomorrow morning.
    (B) She has to prepare for a presentation.
    (C) She has a meeting this afternoon.
    (D) She needs to bring the computer home with her.

9. What does Denise think she'll have to do to correct her problem?
    (A) Stop using computers
    (B) Borrow a computer from her work
    (C) Learn how to fix computers
    (D) Buy a new computer

10. What is the talk mainly about?
    (A) How to download music
    (B) The effects of illegal downloading
    (C) Information related to a genre of music
    (D) Where aboriginal tribesman can be found

11. Which of the following groups is most likely to make world music?
    (A) Rock stars
    (B) Rap singers
    (C) A country's native people
    (D) American jazz musicians

12. Why has downloading been a good thing for world music?
    (A) The singers have become richer.
    (B) More people have access to that music.
    (C) It has made people interested in learning about other cultures.
    (D) World music is now rated on the pop charts.

Part 4 Short Talks

13. What time of the year is it?
    (A) Spring
    (B) Summer
    (C) Autumn
    (D) Winter

14. What problem does the speaker say is caused by the current weather conditions?
    (A) Many cars break down.
    (B) People catch colds.
    (C) People don't exercise.
    (D) People stay home from work.

15. What solution does the speaker suggest?
    (A) People should eat better.
    (B) People should walk in the snow.
    (C) People should stay home more.
    (D) People should spend less money.

16. Who is the speaker probably addressing?
    (A) A group of travelers
    (B) Radio DJs
    (C) People in a supermarket
    (D) Potential clients

17. What advantage does the Opto860HD have over other similar products?
    (A) It is faster.
    (B) It is lighter.
    (C) It is smaller.
    (D) It is brighter.

18. What will happen next?
    (A) The speaker will show a movie.
    (B) The speaker will conclude his presentation.
    (C) The speaker will set up the device.
    (D) The speaker will answer people's questions.

19. How many flavors of pie does Johnny's restaurant offer?
    (A) Ten
    (B) Three
    (C) Eight
    (D) Four

20. What can you do in Johnny's Game Town?
    (A) Drink coffee
    (B) Play video games
    (C) Watch movies
    (D) Make pizzas

21. What is Johnny's Party World doing to celebrate its grand opening?
    (A) Offering a free dessert with every meal
    (B) Offering a free game of bowling
    (C) Offering a free coffee with every meal
    (D) Offering a chance to play video games for free

22. In what type of situation would you most likely hear this announcement?
    (A) Before taking off on a flight
    (B) Before landing at your destination
    (C) In the event of an emergency
    (D) Before purchasing your flight tickets

23. What is the final destination of flight 4465?
    (A) La Guardia
    (B) Denver
    (C) Dallas-Fort Worth
    (D) Los Angeles

24. What does the speaker most likely mean when he says, "got you covered"?
    (A) The crew has blankets available for cold passengers.
    (B) The crew is looking for any type of suspicious activity.
    (C) The crew has everything under control.
    (D) The crew is paying for all of the drinks on the flight.

Part 4 Short Talks

25. Why does the speaker think he may not have ordered enough supplies?
    (A) He has already checked the shipments.
    (B) The company didn't tell him what to order.
    (C) The company hired more people than he expected.
    (D) He saw more people in the boardroom.

Item Receipt	
Product	Quantity
Binder	10
Filing cabinet	7
Desk chair	7
Keyboard	6

26. What does the speaker mean when he says "I've got something for you"?
    (A) He wants to give Noah a task.
    (B) He wants to give Noah a gift.
    (C) He has a secret to tell Noah.
    (D) He has a package that arrived for Noah.

27. Look at the graphic and consider the message. What is the problem with the order?
    (A) They purchased too many of one item.
    (B) They didn't purchase enough of one item.
    (C) They didn't purchase enough of three of the items.
    (D) They didn't purchase enough of any items.

28. Which problem does the speaker mention?
    (A) An accident on the 105
    (B) An accident on the 101
    (C) An accident on Highway 16
    (D) An accident at the Space Needle

29. Look at the graphic. Which of the labeled roads could be Highway 105?
    (A) A   (B) B
    (C) C   (D) D

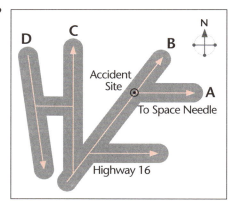

30. What is going to happen next?
    (A) An advertisement is coming up.
    (B) The traffic report will be given.
    (C) The weather will be talked about.
    (D) A song will play.

Part 5 Incomplete Sentences 句子填空

題型介紹

題數	三十題（多益考試兩百題中的第 101~130 題）
題型說明	• 三十題中題題獨立、互不相關。 • 每題句子中會有空格，須從四個選項中選出最適當的答案以完成句子。 • 測驗考生的單字、片語與文法能力。
建議作答時間	12 分鐘
題目範例	1. Customers ------- upset when they discovered the store had run out of the special product a day earlier. 　(A) becomes 　(B) are becoming 〔辨識選項是否為同一個字的變化？〕 　(C) to become 　(D) became ➡ 主詞為 customers、空格處為主要動詞，when ... 為子句。 2. The company ------- that it was spending too much money on snacks, so it was announced that staff would have to start paying for their own. 　(A) replied 　(B) relived 　(C) realized 　(D) respected ➡ 主詞為 the company、空格處為主要動詞，逗點後以連接詞 so 接子句。 正解請見 p.89

基本作答流程與技巧

Step 1 閱讀題目選項及空格前後文
在每題不到 30 秒作答時間的情況下，若每一題都從頭到尾閱讀句子，將難以在時間內完成。故務必要先閱讀題目選項後分辨題型（題型分析請見 p.88）。

Step 2 找出句子主要的主詞和動詞
此大題的句子往往很長，甚至句構會比較複雜，但有時並不需要完整閱讀即可作答。故須養成「化繁為簡」的能力，抓出句子主要的主詞和動詞，以便找出考題重點並有效解題。

Step 3 依題型不同對症下藥
除非空格是須了解整個句子結構或句意才能作答，否則不要浪費時間看完整個題目再作答。如基本詞性題或固定用法的片語等，看完選項及空格前後關鍵字詞後便可立即作答。對於須耗費較多時間的題目應勇敢跳過，務必先做完拿手題型，掌握基本分。

Part 5 Incomplete Sentences

解題步驟與題型分析

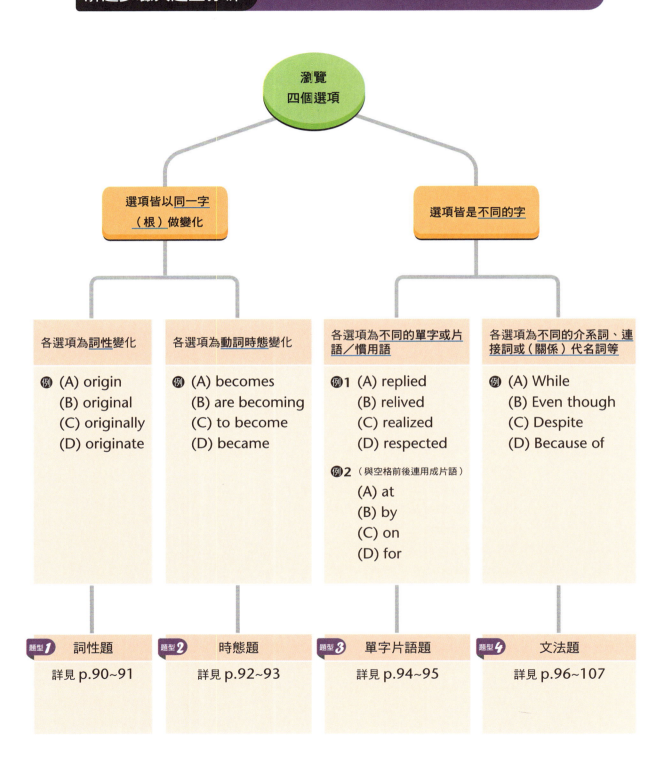

題型	範例	解析
1. 詞性題	The Taj Mahal in India was ------- built in memory of a king's dead wife. (A) origin　　　(B) original (C) originally　(D) originate	空格後為動詞（被動語態），故要填入可修飾動詞的副詞，答案選 (C) originally「原本；起初」。 (A) 名詞「起源；由來」。 (B) 形容詞「最初的；本來的」。 (D) 動詞「來自；產生」。
2. 時態題	Customers ------- upset when they discovered the store had run out of the special product a day earlier. (A) becomes　　(B) are becoming (C) to become　(D) became	本句主詞為 customers，空格內要填入動詞，而從 when... 開始的子句中動詞用過去式 discovered，故主要句的動詞應與子句一致使用過去式，故答案選 (D)。
3. 單字片語題	The company ------- that it was spending too much money on snacks, so it was announced that staff would have to start paying for their own. (A) replied　　(B) relived (C) realized　(D) respected	考單字時常可依句意來判斷適合的答案。本題意為「公司……他們花費太多的費用在甜點上，所以宣布員工得開始自己付費。」，選項皆為過去式，意思分別為： (A) 回答；答覆 (B) 再生；復活 (C) 察覺；領悟到 (D) 尊重；重視 依句意適合的答案選 (C)。
	Speaking ------- behalf of the board and CEO of Unicorp, Kevin Johnson welcomed all visiting guests at the opening ceremony. (A) at　　(B) by (C) on　(D) for	注意空格後的 behalf 這個字，即可發現這裡考慣用語 on behalf of「代替；代表」，因此本題不用讀完整個句子即可馬上選出答案為 (C)。
4. 文法題	------- environmental issues, it is no longer possible for companies to release chemicals into rivers. (A) While　　　(B) Even though (C) Despite　　(D) Because of	空格後 environmental issues「環境議題」為複合名詞，選項 (A) 和 (B) 為從屬連接詞，後面應接子句，故不會是正確答案。因此可能填入的選項只剩 (C) 和 (D)，而依後面句意「企業已不可能排放化學物質進入河川了」可知答案應選具因果含意的 (D) because of「因為；由於」。

Part 5 句子填空

Part 5 Incomplete Sentences

題型 1 詞性題　Syntactic Functions

詞性題在 Part 5 中屬於不用看完句子即可**馬上做答**的題目，只要能正確判斷詞性並具備各詞性功能及在句中位置的概念，便能輕鬆應答，是務必要掌握得分的題型。

各詞性常見結尾

	名詞 n.		動詞 v.	形容詞 adj.	副詞 adv.
常見結尾	-ance / -ancy -ence -ant -ian -ism -ist	-tion / -sion -ment -ness -ship -or / -er -ty / -ity	-ate -en -ify -fy -ize	-able / -ible -ous / ious -ic / -ical -al -ful -ish -ive	-ly -ward -wise
範例	admis**sion**		admit	admiss**ible**	admiss**ibly**
	condi**tion**		condition	condition**al**	conditional**ly**
	critic / critic**ism**		critic**ize**	critic**al**	critical**ly**
	expecta**tion**		expect	expect**able**	expectab**ly**
	inclu**sion**		include	inclus**ive**	inclusive**ly**
	origin		origin**ate**	origin**al**	original**ly**
	specia**list** / specia**lty**		specia**lize**	speci**al**	special**ly**
	specifica**tion**		speci**fy**	specif**ic**	specifical**ly**

各詞性基本概念

詞性	基本概念與用法	範例
名詞	名詞一般在冠詞（a, an, the）、所有格（my, your, his, our, their . . .）、形容詞或量詞（many, much, some . . .）之後。	• Some **companies** have already sent **representatives** to the **conference**. 有幾家公司已經派了代表去參加會議。
	專有名詞（人名、地名等）及**統稱**（如運動類、抽象字等）前通常**不需冠詞**。	• **Paris** is the capital of **France**. 巴黎是法國的首都。 • **Football** is a popular sport in **America**. 橄欖球在美國是一項很受歡迎的運動。

動詞	多用來修飾主詞。動詞與主詞單複數須一致。	• The **box** of pencils **is** on the desk. 那盒鉛筆在書桌上。 • The **pencils are** on the desk. 這些鉛筆在書桌上。
	助動詞（must, do, can, will, should, may 等）後接原形動詞。	• We **should go**. 我們該走了。 • Jody **can type** very fast! 裘蒂打字很快！
形容詞	常用來修飾名詞。	• Kate is a **smart** student. 凱特是一名聰明的學生。
	大部分的規則動詞加 -ed 或 -ing 即成為形容詞。	• love (v.) ➡ loved 被愛的 　　　　　　➡ loving 鍾愛的；深情的
副詞	可修飾動詞、形容詞或另一個副詞。	• Tommy sings **well**. 湯米歌唱得很好。 • Susan is **really** beautiful. 蘇珊真的很美。 • Jeremy speaks English **pretty** well. 傑若米英文說得很好。
	位置多元，可置於句首／中／尾，用來修飾一個片語、子句或句子。	• **Certainly**, I will be your best friend forever. 無疑地，我永遠都會是你最好的朋友。 • My mother came back home **soon** after work. 我母親下班後很快地就回到家了。

Exercise

A word or phrase is missing in each of the sentences below. Select the best answer to complete the sentence.

1. Jill put her money into stocks because they are good -------.
   (A) investors　　(B) invest　　(C) investing　　(D) investments
   Your answer: Ⓐ Ⓑ Ⓒ Ⓓ

2. Roy Garside was asked to purchase two seats by the airline due to his ------- weight.
   (A) consideration　(B) considered　(C) consider　(D) considerable
   Your answer: Ⓐ Ⓑ Ⓒ Ⓓ

Part 5 Incomplete Sentences

題型 2 時態題 Verb Tenses

瀏覽四個選項看到皆屬同一個動詞,但以不同時式出現,便知為考時態的題型。以下為各種時態的整理歸納。

時態與例句		常搭配使用的時間副詞或詞彙
簡單式 (過去簡單式 / 現在簡單式 / 未來簡單式 past—now—future)		
現在簡單式	• He often **eats** noodles. 他常吃麵。	always, usually, often, sometimes, seldom, never, every day/week, on the weekends
過去簡單式	• He **ate** noodles yesterday. 他昨天吃了麵。	yesterday, last week/weekend/year, three days ago, the other day
未來簡單式	• He **will eat** noodles tomorrow. = He **is going to eat** noodles tomorrow. 他明天會吃麵。	this Sunday/weekend, tomorrow morning/evening, next Monday/week/month, in ten minutes, in three days, in an hour
進行式 (過去進行式 / 現在進行式 / 未來進行式 past—now—future)		
現在進行式	• He **is eating** noodles right now. 他現在正在吃麵。	currently, continually, constantly, right now, at the present time
過去進行式	• He **was eating** noodles when I came home. 我回家時他正在吃麵。	at that time, about this time last week/month/year 說明 常搭配過去某個時間的副詞、副詞片語或副詞子句。
未來進行式	• He **will be eating** noodles when I go home tonight. 我今晚回家時,他將會在吃麵。	說明 常搭配表示未來時間的副詞、副詞片語或副詞子句。

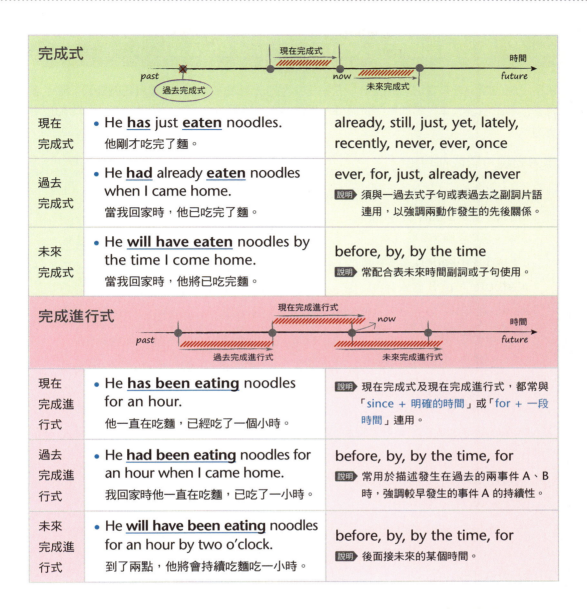

Exercise

A word or phrase is missing in each of the sentences below. Select the best answer to complete the sentence.

1. The manager thinks the way Trevor ------- recently is rather strange.
   (A) act　　　(B) will be acting　(C) had acted　　(D) has been acting
   Your answer: Ⓐ Ⓑ Ⓒ Ⓓ

2. Since 1994, there ------- many attempts to change the way we see our environment.
   (A) are　　　(B) has been　　　(C) have been　　(D) had been
   Your answer: Ⓐ Ⓑ Ⓒ Ⓓ

題型 3　單字片語題　Vocabulary and Phrases

單字片語的題型近來有增加的趨勢，占考題中大約三到四成。這一類題目範圍廣泛，除了多背多益考試出現頻率較高的單字片語外，平時亦應多接觸英文相關的媒體報章，以增加應考實力。

常考動詞片語或慣用語　🎧 Track 93

- ☐ agree/disagree with 同意／不同意
- ☐ aim to + V. / aim at + Ving 企圖；意欲；瞄準目標
- ☐ attend a meeting 參與會議
- ☐ attribute A to B 將 A 歸因於 B
- ☐ be accessible to 可進入；可取得
- ☐ be against 反對
- ☐ be capable of + N./Ving 有……的能力
- ☐ be exposed to 暴露於……之中
- ☐ be familiar to + sb. 對某人而言是熟悉的
- ☐ be familiar with + N. 熟悉某人／事／物
- ☐ be in favor of 支持
- ☐ be included in 包含；納入
- ☐ be known for 因……有名
- ☐ be made available 使可用的
- ☐ be subject to 以……為條件；取決於；須經
- ☐ borrow from 向……借
- ☐ break one's promise 打破承諾
- ☐ catch up (with) 趕上（進度等）
- ☐ close/shut down 歇業；停工
- ☐ conduct a survey 進行調查
- ☐ convince sb. of sth. 讓某人相信某事
- ☐ dedicate to 致力於
- ☐ depend/rely on 依賴、端視……
- ☐ distinguish A from B 區別 A 與 B
- ☐ distribute to 分配；分發
- ☐ earn a degree 獲得學位
- ☐ execute/implement a plan 執行計畫
- ☐ give/deliver a speech 發表演說
- ☐ have good/great taste in sth. 對某事物有品味
- ☐ lend/loan to 借錢給……；貸款給……
- ☐ make automatic withdrawals 自動轉帳
- ☐ offer a discount 提供折扣
- ☐ open for business 開幕；營業
- ☐ place an order 下訂單
- ☐ play an important role 扮演重要的角色
- ☐ receive an award 獲獎
- ☐ run out of 用完；耗盡
- ☐ schedule/reschedule an appointment （重新）預約時間
- ☐ show up 出現
- ☐ take responsibility for 負起責任

常考名詞片語或詞組　🎧 Track 94

- ☐ assembly/factory/production line 生產線
- ☐ award ceremony 頒獎典禮
- ☐ board of directors 董事會
- ☐ budget cut 預算削減
- ☐ car parts 汽車零件
- ☐ common practice 慣例

- ☐ day/night shift 日／夜班
- ☐ express delivery 快遞
- ☐ job interview 求職面試
- ☐ job opening 職缺
- ☐ labor cost 人力（勞動）成本
- ☐ office personnel/staff 辦公室員工
- ☐ office regulation 辦公室規則
- ☐ office supplies 辦公用品
- ☐ overnight delivery 隔夜快遞
- ☐ power supply 電源
- ☐ promotion strategy 推廣／宣傳策略
- ☐ retirement party 退休招待會

其他常考慣用語 　Track 95

- ☐ a large amount of 大量的
- ☐ a variety of 多種的；多樣的
- ☐ in terms of 就……而言
- ☐ it's time to . . . 是……的時候
- ☐ on behalf of sb. 代表某人
- ☐ thanks to 由於

Exercise

A word or phrase is missing in each of the sentences below. Select the best answer to complete the sentence.

1. Jamal had to ------- his doctor's appointment because he got out of his meeting three hours late.
   (A) react
   (B) reduce
   (C) reinvent
   (D) reschedule
   Your answer: Ⓐ Ⓑ Ⓒ Ⓓ

2. We have a large ------- of our money tied up in the house, so we can't afford any big purchases.
   (A) number
   (B) figure
   (C) amount
   (D) total
   Your answer: Ⓐ Ⓑ Ⓒ Ⓓ

3. Harry took ------- his actions and told the truth about taking the office supplies.
   (A) response to
   (B) responsibility for
   (C) responsible to
   (D) reputable for
   Your answer: Ⓐ Ⓑ Ⓒ Ⓓ

題型 4　文法題　Grammar

文法題占多益考題比例約有三成。以下針對多益常考的文法重點做整理歸納及練習。

文法重點 1：被動語態

基本句型： **be 動詞 + 過去分詞（p.p.）**

簡單式的被動語態

時態	結構	例句
現在簡單式	am / is / are + p.p.	Cigarettes **are known** to cause cancer. 一般認為香菸會致癌。
過去簡單式	was / were + p.p.	Many houses **were destroyed** in the flood. 許多房子在洪水中被摧毀。
未來簡單式	will be + p.p.	These books **will be thrown out** if no one claims them. 這些書如果沒有人認領的話就會被丟掉。

完成式的被動語態

時態	結構	例句
現在完成式	has / have + been + p.p.	The criminal **has been arrested** by the police. 這名罪犯已被警方逮捕。
過去完成式	had been + p.p.	Josh **had been fired** twice by the time he was thirty. 在賈許三十歲之前，他已經被解僱過兩次了。
未來完成式	will have been + p.p.	By the time you arrive, a room **will have been prepared** for you. 在你到達前，房間就會幫你準備好。

進行式的被動語態

時態	結構	例句
現在進行式	am / is / are + being + p.p.	The show **is being watched** by millions of people around the world. 這場表演正被全球各地數百萬人觀賞著。
過去進行式	was / were + being + p.p.	The employees **were being lectured** by their boss when the visitor arrived. 這位訪客到達時，這些員工正被他們的老闆訓斥。

文法重點 2：反身代名詞

用法：1. 主詞與受詞同一人時，可使用反身代名詞作受詞用。
　　　2. 可放在名詞或代名詞之後作為強調。

第一人稱	單數	myself
	複數	ourselves
第二人稱	單數	yourself
	複數	yourselves
第三人稱	單數陽性	himself
	單數陰性	herself
	單數中性（事物）	itself
	複數	themselves

例 I would like to design a house **myself** one day.
有一天我要自己設計一間房子。

例 I did it **myself**. Don't blame anyone else.
是我自己要做的。不要怪其他人。

例 He bought **himself** a car.
他給自己買了一輛車。

例 The program can turn **itself** off at the end of the day.
一天結束時，這個程式能自動關閉。

Exercise

A word or phrase is missing in each of the sentences below. Select the best answer to complete the sentence.

1. People are ------- not to move a person who has had a serious accident, as it could make any injuries worse.
   (A) advise　　　　　　　　　　(B) advises
   (C) advised　　　　　　　　　 (D) to advise
   Your answer: Ⓐ Ⓑ Ⓒ Ⓓ

2. The teenagers thought they could do it -------, but they actually needed help from their parents.
   (A) they　　　　　　　　　　　(B) themselves
   (C) them　　　　　　　　　　　(D) theirs
   Your answer: Ⓐ Ⓑ Ⓒ Ⓓ

3. My motorcycle ------- for service yesterday, as I had been having problems with the brakes.
   (A) is taken　　　　　　　　　　(B) was take
   (C) was have　　　　　　　　　 (D) was taken in
   Your answer: Ⓐ Ⓑ Ⓒ Ⓓ

Part 5 Incomplete Sentences

文法重點 3：介系詞

表時間的介系詞

at + （一天中的）某鐘點、某時間點 on + 星期幾、特定的某日（包括某日上午、下午或傍晚） in + 較長的一段時間	例 I usually study **at** night because I work during the day. 我通常晚上唸書因為我白天工作。 例 My appointment is **on** Tuesday afternoon. 我是預約星期二下午。
by / no later than + 某時間點	例 Come to the office **by / no later than** nine o'clock. 九點鐘之前來公司。
till / until / up to + 某時間點	例 Karen's school continues **until / up to** the end of next month. 凱倫的學校要持續上課到下個月底。
during / throughout + 某段時間／某個活動期間 through / over + 某段時間／某個活動期間 from + 某時間點 + to/till/until + 某時間點	例 I drink coffee **throughout** the day. 我一整天都在喝咖啡。 例 I will be in New York **over** the weekend. 我週末的時候會在紐約。 例 This café is crowded **from** morning **till** evening. 這家咖啡館從早到晚都擠滿人。
for + 一段時間 since + 過去某個時間點	例 Jillian has been an employee of Elite Co. **for** four years. 姬莉安任職於伊利特公司已經四年了。

表空間的介系詞

表位置： above、at、before、behind、below、beneath、by、in、on、over、under	例 The presenter drew a diagram **on** the whiteboard. 該名簡報者在白板上畫了一個圖表。 例 A giant balloon is floating **over** the stadium. 一顆大氣球正飄過體育館的上空。
表方向： across、along、around、down、for、from、in、into、off、out of、through、to、toward、up	例 The man was walking **along** the side of the river. 這名男子沿著河邊行走。 例 The rabbit jumped **down** the hole. 兔子跳下洞裡。 例 The fireman ran **into** the burning building. 消防員衝進失火的大樓。

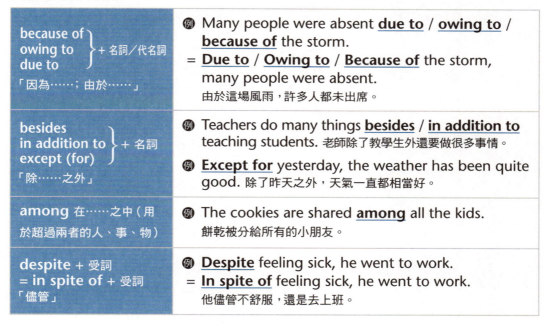

Exercise

A word or phrase is missing in each of the sentences below. Select the best answer to complete the sentence.

1. Frank is taking a break ------- our being in a hurry.
   (A) toward　　(B) despite　　(C) above　　(D) through
   Your answer: Ⓐ Ⓑ Ⓒ Ⓓ

2. ------- our annual meeting, we were interrupted by a fire alarm.
   (A) Until　　(B) Besides　　(C) Around　　(D) During
   Your answer: Ⓐ Ⓑ Ⓒ Ⓓ

Part 5　Incomplete Sentences

文法重點 4：連接詞

連接詞乃是連接字與字、片語與片語、子句與子句或句子與句子之間。一般分為：「對等連接詞」、「從屬連接詞」和「連接副詞」。

對等連接詞

對等連接詞： and、but、or、so、for、yet、nor	例 You don't have the training for the job, **nor** do you have the experience. 你沒有受過做這份工作的訓練，也沒有經驗。 說明 nor 連接的句子需要倒裝。
配對連接詞： both . . . and、not . . . but、not only . . . but also、either . . . or、neither . . . nor	例 The research project will take **both** time **and** money. 研究企劃需要花時間和金錢。 例 I'll take **either** chemistry **or** physics next semester. 我下學期不是修化學課就是選物理課。

從屬連接詞

引導「時間」： as、while、when、before、by the time (that)、after、as soon as、once、the moment that、until、since、no sooner than 等	例 I lost my ring **when/while** I was washing the dishes. 我在洗碗的時候弄丟了戒指。 例 **As soon as** I smelled the food, I got hungry. 一聞到食物的味道，我就餓了。
引導「狀態」： as、as if、as though	例 The woman looks at the man **as if** she knows who he is. 這個女人看著這個男人彷彿知道他的身份。
引導「原因」： because、since、as、now that 等	例 **Since/Because/As** I practice yoga every day, I have a lot of energy. 由於我每天練瑜珈，所以精力充沛。
引導「結果」： so . . . that、such . . . that、so/such . . . as to	例 It's **such** nice weather **that** we may go hiking. 天氣這麼好，我們可以去健行。
引導「目的」： so that、in order that 等	例 **In order that** you may demonstrate your skills, we have devised a test for you. 為了讓你能展示你的技能，我們為你設計了一項測驗。
引導「對比」： while、whereas	例 Karen has a great sense of humor and loves to laugh, **whereas** Susan is a rather serious and quiet girl. 凱倫有絕佳幽默感、喜歡笑，而蘇珊則是個相當嚴肅、安靜的女生。

引導「讓步」：although、though、even though 等	例 **Even though** the whole town contributed, there still wasn't enough money to rebuild the school. 即使所有的鎮民都樂捐了，但還是沒有足夠的錢來重建學校。
引導「條件」：if、unless、in case (that)、provided (that)、providing (that)、given (that)、on condition that、only if、as long as	例 We expect the factory's output to increase, **provided/providing (that)** we train enough workers. 我們希望工廠的產能會增加，只要我們能訓練足夠員工的話。 例 **Given (that)** the voters approved the use of funds, we should start construction plans soon. 投票人已核准了資金的使用，我們應該要盡快開始進行興建計畫了。

連接副詞

表「推論或結果」：accordingly、as a result、consequently、hence、therefore、thus	例 The other scientists are senior to us; **accordingly**, their experiments get first priority in the laboratory. 其他的科學家都比我們資深，因此，他們的研究計畫在實驗室裡都較為優先。
表「反義或對照」：by contrast、however、nonetheless、nevertheless、on the contrary	例 He is not poor; **on the contrary**, he is a millionaire. 他不窮，相反地，他是個百萬富翁。
表「總結」：all in all、in brief、in conclusion、in short、in sum、in summary、to sum up	例 Our opponents had more experience and better training. **In short**, we were outclassed. 我們的對手有較多的經驗和較好的訓練。簡而言之，我們被比下去了。

Exercise

A word or phrase is missing in each of the sentences below. Select the best answer to complete the sentence.

1. ------- preparing to go to university, Jenny took the time to learn some other skills to help her get a part-time job.
   (A) Thus　　(B) Unless　　(C) While　　(D) By contrast
   Your answer: Ⓐ Ⓑ Ⓒ Ⓓ

2. Many people claim that they want to lose weight, ------- they don't do any exercise.
   (A) and　　(B) so　　(C) yet　　(D) nor
   Your answer: Ⓐ Ⓑ Ⓒ Ⓓ

文法重點 5：分詞

分為兩大類：1. Ving 現在分詞（表「主動、進行」）
　　　　　　2. p.p. 過去分詞（表「被動、完成」）

分詞作形容詞用

現在分詞 （Ving）	• 表示「令人覺得……的」 • 描述某人或某事引起的感受	例 Soaking in a hot spring is very **relaxing**. 泡溫泉讓人覺得很放鬆。 例 The horror movie was very **frightening**. 這部恐怖電影很嚇人。
過去分詞 （p.p.）	• 表示「感到、覺得……的」 • 描述某人所經歷的感受	例 After going on holiday, Todd is now very **relaxed**. 塔德在度完假後，現在感到很放鬆。 例 Alicia was **frightened** after watching the horror movie. 愛莉西亞看完恐怖電影後被嚇到了。

分詞作受詞補語

S. + find + O. + { Ving（主動） 　 p.p.（被動） 發現（某人事物）……	例 Robbie came home late and **found** his father **waiting** for him. 羅比晚歸發現父親正在等他。 例 The refugees tried to return home, only to **find** their homes **destroyed**. 這些難民試圖重返家園，結果卻發現家園已毀。
S. + find + O. + (to be) + adj. 覺得（某人事物）……	例 The actress **found** the reporter's questions (to be) **annoying**. 這位女演員覺得記者的問題很討人厭。
S. + keep + O. + { Ving（主動） 　 p.p.（被動） 　 adj. 使……處於……狀態中	例 Don't **keep** me **waiting** too long. 別讓我等太久。 例 The Internet **keeps** us **updated** on news from around the world. 網路讓我們可隨時得知世界各地最新的消息。 例 John hired a maid to **keep** his house **clean**. 約翰雇了一名女僕來維持家裡的清潔。
S. + leave + O. + { Ving（主動） 　 p.p.（被動） 　 adj. 任由……處於……狀態中	例 Mark **left** his car **running** while he went into the shop. 馬克進入商店時，他讓車子發動著沒熄火。 例 Tina always **leaves** her shoelaces **undone**. 緹娜總是不綁鞋帶。 例 After the dog tried to bite them, the boys decided to **leave** it **alone**. 這群男孩在狗試圖咬他們後，決定不再理牠。

分詞構句

連接詞 + S. + V., S. + V.
   副詞子句   主要子句

改→ { Ving / p.p. }, S. + V.
           主要子句

改→ { After / Before } + { Ving / p.p. }, S. + V.
                       主要子句

例 **Because she was late** for work, Karen skipped breakfast.

改→ **Being late** for work, Karen skipped breakfast.

凱倫因為上班遲到所以沒吃早餐。

例 **Before he cleaned** his room, Johnny washed his dirty clothes.

改→ **Before cleaning** his room, Johnny washed his dirty clothes.

強尼在打掃房間之前，先洗了他的髒衣服。

Exercise

A word or phrase is missing in each of the sentences below. Select the best answer to complete the sentence.

1. After climbing the mountain, the team was -------.
   (A) exhausting
   (B) exhausted
   (C) exhaust
   (D) to exhaust
   Your answer: Ⓐ Ⓑ Ⓒ Ⓓ

2. As the detective was ------- the room, he discovered a clue.
   (A) investigating
   (B) investigated
   (C) being investigated
   (D) to investigate
   Your answer: Ⓐ Ⓑ Ⓒ Ⓓ

3. ------- into account his performance, I suggest we start looking for another sales assistant.
   (A) Taken
   (B) Be taking
   (C) Taking
   (D) Take
   Your answer: Ⓐ Ⓑ Ⓒ Ⓓ

文法重點 6：關係詞

關係子句指兩句中皆有一個相同意義的字詞，要合併兩句，就要找出兩句中的「關係」，並且用關係詞將兩句合併成一句，形成關係子句，故關係詞具有連接詞的功能。以下簡介常見的關係詞的種類及用法。

關係代名詞

	主格	受格	所有格
人	who/(that)	whom/(that)	whose
事物	which/(that)	which/(that)	whose（今較常用） of which（今較少用）
人、事物	that	that	✗
例句	• Employees **who/that** are coming on the trip must sign up by Friday. 要參加旅遊的員工必須在星期五以前登記。 • The building **which/that** was on fire is very close to my office. 那棟失火的建築離我的辦公室很近。	• It is Dr. Alan **whom/that** Ben is meeting on Friday. 班星期五是跟艾倫博士碰面。 • The things **which/that** John loves are music and soccer. 約翰喜歡的東西是音樂和足球。	• The employee **whose** phone is ringing is out sick today. 電話在響的這名員工今天生病沒來。 • The computer **whose** mouse was broken hadn't been used by anyone in weeks. 那部電腦的滑鼠壞掉，已經幾個星期都沒有人使用了。

關係副詞

when	• Three-thirty is usually the time **when** the mailman delivers the mail. 三點半通常是郵差送信的時間。
where	• The restaurant **where** we were supposed to meet was closed. 我們要約見面的餐廳已經關了。
why	• The weather is cold, which is the reason **why** there are so many people sick. 天氣很冷，這也就是有這麼多人生病的原因。
how	• Do a little work every day. This is **how** you can finish any project, no matter its size. 每天做一點，這就是你能完成任何專案的方式，不論案子有多大。

複合關係詞

whoever	• **Whoever** answers the phone should be able to help you. 任何接電話的人應該都可以協助你。
whichever	• I just need a phone that works. I'll take **whichever** is the cheapest. 我只需要能用的電話。不論哪支，我會選最便宜的那一支。
whomever	• You may invite **whomever** you like, but you can only invite one person. 你可以邀請任何人，但只能邀請一個。
whatever	• When it comes to clothes, my sisters just buy **whatever** is on sale. 說到買衣服，我的姊妹們只買打折的衣服。
whenever	• We will be leaving **whenever** the rest of the group shows up. 這個團體裡的其他人一到我們就會出發。
wherever	• Peter is very charming and outgoing, and he makes friends **wherever** he goes. 彼得迷人又活潑，不論到哪裡他都能交到朋友。
however	• You can rearrange the furniture **however** you think it should be. 你可以把家具重新擺設成你想要的樣子。

Exercise

A word or phrase is missing in each of the sentences below. Select the best answer to complete the sentence.

1. Topo Beverages, ------- was established just two years ago, is already a major player in the industry.
   (A) who   (B) which   (C) where   (D) why
   Your answer: Ⓐ Ⓑ Ⓒ Ⓓ

2. ------- Dan is in town, he pays a visit to his old neighborhood and hangs out with his childhood friends.
   (A) Whatever   (B) However   (C) Whenever   (D) Whoever
   Your answer: Ⓐ Ⓑ Ⓒ Ⓓ

3. Karl Grayson, ------- has been with us for over 10 years, is the best man for the job.
   (A) who   (B) whose   (C) which   (D) where
   Your answer: Ⓐ Ⓑ Ⓒ Ⓓ

文法重點 7：假設語氣

if 引導的假設句可分為

與現在事實相反

表「現在幾乎不可能或完全不可能發生的事實或願望」。

if 子句	主要子句
If + S. + 過去式,	S. + could / might / should / would + V.
If + S. + were ...,	

- 例 If I **had** the money, I **would set up** an organization to help natural disaster victims. 如果我現在有資金，我會成立一個組織來幫助天災受害者。

- 例 If Sean **were** more patient, he **could sell** his house for a better price.
  倒裝▸ **Were** Sean more patient, he **could sell** his house for a better price.
  如果尚恩有多一點耐性的話，他就可以把房子賣到更好的價錢。

與過去事實相反

表「過去並未發生的事實、或是過去未能實現的願望」。

if 子句	主要子句
If + S. + had + p.p.	S. + could / might / should / would + have + p.p.

- 例 If Dan **had told** me about the meeting, I **would have finished** the report earlier.
  倒裝▸ **Had** Dan **told** me about the meeting, I **would have finished** the report earlier.
  要是丹有告訴我要開會，我就會早一點把報告完成了。

過去的假設影響到現在的結果

if 子句	主要子句
If + S. + had + p.p.	S. + could / might / should / would + V.

> 例 If Sam **had left** the company, he **wouldn't have** the great salary he has now.
> 如果山姆當初離開這家公司，現在他就不會擁有這麼優渥的薪水。

與未來事實相反

表「未來並不可能發生，或發生的機率非常低」。

if 子句	主要子句
If + S. + were to + V.	S. + could / might / should / would + V.

> 例 If Lester **were to** finish his novel, he **could sell** it for a lot of money.
> 如果萊斯特完成小說的話，他將能賣得一大筆錢。

> 例 If the sun **were to** rise in the west, I **would marry** you.
> 如果太陽從西邊出來，我就嫁給你。

對未來某事抱持強烈懷疑時，亦可用假設法未來式，表「萬一……的話」。

if 子句	主要子句
If + S. + should + V.	S. + 過去式助動詞 + V.
	S. + 助動詞 + V.
	祈使句

> 例 If you **should** find out the game's score, you **could call** me and **tell** me.
> 萬一你知道比賽的分數，可以打電話告訴我。

> 例 If you **should** go to the post office, you **can buy** some stamps for me.
> 萬一你有到郵局的話，可以幫我買一些郵票。

Exercise

A word or phrase is missing in each of the sentences below. Select the best answer to complete the sentence.

1. If the Thompsons ------- to come, we would have more people than chairs.
   (A) are (B) were (C) could (D) should
   Your answer: Ⓐ Ⓑ Ⓒ Ⓓ

2. ------- you have any further questions, please contact us at 777-8407.
   (A) Would (B) Could (C) Should (D) Have
   Your answer: Ⓐ Ⓑ Ⓒ Ⓓ

Part 5 Incomplete Sentences

Practice Test PART 5

Directions:
A word or phrase is missing in each of the sentences below. Four answer choices are given below each sentence. Select the best answer to complete the sentence. Then mark the letter (A), (B), (C), or (D) on your answer sheet.

1. ------- there had been an announcement made about the change in procedure, Richard wouldn't have kept following the old guidelines.
   (A) Had   (B) Unless
   (C) Whereas   (D) If

2. On hearing about the emergency, the president ------- the nation via a live television broadcast.
   (A) delivered
   (B) transmitted
   (C) forwarded
   (D) addressed

3. One of the strangest bicycles ever devised was the "Penny Farthing" ------- was famous for an oversized front wheel and a much smaller wheel at the rear.
   (A) who   (B) what
   (C) where   (D) which

4. In ------- of quality, there is nothing better than the bread from that bakery.
   (A) fact   (B) order
   (C) terms   (D) addition

5. We ------- to include a new feature in the magazine, but in the end our readers told us that it was not what they wanted.
   (A) were going   (B) have been
   (C) was going   (D) had been

6. Most people in this part of the country rely ------- farming to support their families.
   (A) for   (B) in
   (C) on   (D) by

108

7. The World Cup ------- every four years but in a different four year cycle to the Olympics.
   (A) was hold
   (B) is held
   (C) was holding
   (D) being held

8. ------- it was first completed, the Channel Tunnel joining England and France was thought of as a marvel of engineering.
   (A) Who
   (B) When
   (C) That
   (D) Which

9. ------- to magazines are falling year on year because of the vast amount of information available on the Internet.
   (A) Subscriptions
   (B) Substitutions
   (C) Descriptions
   (D) Generations

10. During his presentation, Lionel ------- looked at his notes, which made him appear nervous.
    (A) frequency
    (B) frequent
    (C) frequently
    (D) frequencies

11. People who bought homes they could not afford have only ------- to blame if they can no longer keep up with mortgage payments.
    (A) himself
    (B) themselves
    (C) herself
    (D) them

12. The city government is ------- that the summer fair will be a huge success, as many tickets have been sold.
    (A) expect
    (B) expectation
    (C) expected
    (D) expecting

Part 5 Incomplete Sentences

13. The ------- meal for the Jewish festival of Rosh Hashanah is apples dipped in honey to symbolize a sweet new year.
    (A) tradition
    (B) traditionalism
    (C) traditional
    (D) traditionally

14. After some painstaking -------, we were able to bring back the seventeenth-century table to its former glory.
    (A) designing
    (B) decoration
    (C) renovation
    (D) redevelopment

15. We ------- all résumés by the 4th of this month and then offer an interview to all suitable candidates.
    (A) reviewed
    (B) will review
    (C) would have reviewed
    (D) reviewing

16. Our charity ------- to promote a sustainable future for people from all walks of life, not just those with large bank accounts.
    (A) targets
    (B) enjoys
    (C) aims
    (D) keeps

17. ------- our office has been underperforming, the president has decided to lay off 15 percent of the staff over the next six months.
    (A) By contrast
    (B) Only if
    (C) Yet
    (D) As

18. ------- The restaurant will be closed on Saturday and will ------- business again on Wednesday.
    (A) open
    (B) open up
    (C) open for
    (D) opening

19. Sales of the new tablet are sure to ------- in the next six months because of a great advertising campaign.
    (A) evaluate
    (B) plummet
    (C) increase
    (D) purchase

20. After his experiences in the business world, Steven Green wrote a(n) ------- of motivational books that were designed to help people realize their goals.
    (A) serial
    (B) series
    (C) episode
    (D) large

21. Market forces dictate what products will continue to be ------- in the future.
    (A) popular
    (B) popularize
    (C) popularity
    (D) popularly

22. ------- Elite Tech. will invest $2.5 million; later it will invest another $5.5 million.
    (A) Belatedly
    (B) Previously
    (C) Initially
    (D) Obviously

23. After spending several years devoting ------- to his studies, Harold received his PhD.
    (A) himself
    (B) herself
    (C) themselves
    (D) oneself

24. ------- it was designed as a way to access important information, the Internet is used mainly for social networking and playing games these days.
    (A) Due to
    (B) However
    (C) In contrast
    (D) Although

Part 5 Incomplete Sentences

25. In order to cut fuel costs, the new car we buy should be as ------- as possible.
    (A) active
    (B) efficient
    (C) capable
    (D) professional

26. If you try many times and don't get it right, be sure to check the -------.
    (A) instructions
    (B) installments
    (C) interruption
    (D) institutions

27. ------- we've assumed for many years that Pluto was another planet, scientists now claim it is a moon.
    (A) Thus
    (B) Before
    (C) Since
    (D) Though

28. Surprisingly, the smartphone ------- has made many people less able to communicate face to face.
    (A) theory
    (B) combination
    (C) commuter
    (D) revolution

29. After several hours of -------, the government still hadn't arrived at a decision about energy prices.
    (A) neglect
    (B) negotiation
    (C) negative
    (D) production

30. In order to obtain your license, you need a completed application form, your passport, and a bill stating your ------- address.
    (A) modern
    (B) nowadays
    (C) current
    (D) contemporary

Part 6　Text Completion 段落填空

題型介紹

題數	十六題（多益考試兩百題中的第 131~146 題）
題型說明	• 由四篇文章組成，每篇有 4 題填空題，整個大題共 16 題。 • 文章中會有空格，須從四個選項中選出最適當的答案。 • 與 Part 5 類似，旨在測驗考生的字彙、文法能力及對文意的理解。唯題型由句子變成段落文章，且加入將完整句填入短文的題型。
建議作答時間	8 分鐘（每題至多 30 秒）

基本作答技巧

Tip 1　辨識題型
先看問題／空格所在的句子及答案選項，並辨識題型（題型分析方式參照 Part 5 p.88）。

Tip 2　若能立即解題就不要浪費時間閱讀上下文
若該題為「詞性題」或「片語題」，只需看空格前後的字詞或空格所在的句子便可立刻答題，作答後便馬上移至下一道題目，將時間省下來留給需要閱讀上下文句子的題型。

Tip 3　須閱讀空格前後文的題型
若看了空格所在的句子後仍無法答題，就閱讀空格所在句之前後句，了解上下文關係或文章脈絡後再進行答題。例如有些「文法題」須根據上下文來判斷應選哪一種連接詞（如表對等、轉折或因果等）。「句子插入題」亦須了解前後文的句意連貫及脈絡。

小提醒　Part 5 提到閱讀句子或文章時須養成「化繁為簡」的能力。尤其在面對 Part 6 須閱讀空格前後文才能作答的題型時，務必要先<u>找出句子主要的主詞和動詞</u>，才能清楚分析文章脈絡並有效解題。以下為將句子「化繁為簡」的範例：

The letter concerning your business idea, which you asked me to type
　　S.　　　補充說明 letter 主旨　　　　補充說明是哪一封 letter

a few days ago, was sent to everyone by messenger last night.
　補充說明時間　　V.　　　O.　　補充 sent 方式　補充 sent 的時間

➡ 化繁為簡後：The letter was sent (to everyone).

Part 6 Text Completion

題目範例與解析

Part 6 空格所考的題型,與 Part 5 大同小異,亦包括考詞性、單字片語及文法等題型,另外還新增句子插入題。現在就透過以下範例練習解題技巧。

Questions 1-3 *refer to the following notice.*

Notice to All Residents

As all of you are aware, last week's storm caused major damage to a lot of the surrounding area's power lines. ---**1**---. Unfortunately, due to maintenance work in the neighborhood, the main electricity will be down from 8 p.m. tonight until 5 a.m. tomorrow morning. Luckily, you don't need to worry about getting up and down the stairs in the dark as the building's utilities, lights, and elevator will all be running off a standby generator. As for your household ---**2**---, they will lose power. The cold temperatures at the moment mean your food and drinks should keep until the power comes back on tomorrow. ---**3**---, if you are concerned about this, we have provided a communal refrigerator on the 12th floor which will stay powered by the standby generator. We apologize for any ---**4**--- caused. If you have any questions or problems, don't hesitate to contact us at 944-7501.

Regards,

The Management

---

1. (A) This was the second storm of the year.
    (B) This week the city is sending electricians to repair the damage.
    (C) Next week we are expected to have much better weather.
    (D) City officials have warned not to drive over any wires.

> **句子插入題**
>
> 選項為四個句子,空格前一句提到暴風雨對周圍環境的電線造成很大的損壞,接著下一句提到要進行維修工作,而選項 (B) 提到會有專業人員來進行修復的工作,與上下文語意連貫,故為正確答案。
>
> 此題型須先閱讀空格的前一句和後一句,根據上下文意找出最符合邏輯及文章脈絡的句子。

2. (A) applications
   (B) appliances
   (C) approaches
   (D) approvals

   單字片語題

   選項中為四個不同的單字，由空格前的形容詞 household「家用的」與該句提到「將會沒電」（will lose power），可知這裡所講的應該是 household appliances「家用電器」，故答案選 (B)。

    若是熟悉 household appliances 這個常用搭配詞彙的話，便可迅速選出答案後立即進行下一道題目。

3. (A) Therefore
   (B) Likewise
   (C) However
   (D) Furthermore

   文法題

   由前面文意可知「目前的低溫足以保存食物和飲水直到隔天電力恢復」（表毋須擔心前文中所說的電器會沒電），而空格後卻接「若您有疑慮，我們在 12 樓提供了公用冰箱」，因此空格內應是轉折語氣的連接詞，故答案選 (C) However「然而；不過」。選項 (A) 為「因此；所以」，表因果；選項 (B) 指「同樣地；照樣地」；選項 (D) 指「而且；此外」，三者都沒有轉折語氣的效果，故與文意不符。

    這裡須閱讀空格之前一句，了解上下文關係後再進行答題。

4. (A) inconvenient
   (B) inconvenienced
   (C) inconveniently
   (D) inconvenience

   詞性題

   空格前面為量詞 any，量詞後常接名詞，而空格後面的 caused 乃用來修飾空格處，因此可迅速推斷空格應填為名詞的選項 (D)。

    務必利用詞性題節省作答時間，將多出來的秒數分配給須閱讀上下文才能作答的題型。

Part 6 Text Completion

多益必備詞彙

以下整理多益應考的必備詞彙，務必熟記以增加字彙能力。

常考動詞片語或慣用語
🎧 Track 96

- ☐ assume responsibility 擔起責任
- ☐ be dominated by 由……操控
- ☐ be eager to V. 渴望做某事
- ☐ be in charge of 負責
- ☐ be out of order 故障
- ☐ be out of service 暫停服務
- ☐ exhibit talent 展現才華
- ☐ feel free to V. 隨意去做某事
- ☐ has earned a reputation 贏得讚譽
- ☐ intend to V. 打算做某事
- ☐ keep a low/high profile 低調／維持高知名度
- ☐ lead a discussion 主導討論
- ☐ look forward to Ving 期盼
- ☐ make/leave a good impression (on sb.) 給（某人）好印象
- ☐ make a note of 把……記下來
- ☐ meet a/the deadline 趕上截止日期
- ☐ pay attention to 注意
- ☐ remind sb. of sth. 提醒某人記住某事
- ☐ replace A with B 以 B 取代 A
- ☐ sb. be hesitant to 某人對於……猶豫不決
- ☐ sb. be promoted to 某人升職為
- ☐ sth. goes according to plan 某事按照計畫進行

名詞片語或詞組
🎧 Track 97

- ☐ budget constraint 預算的限制
- ☐ business skill 商業技巧
- ☐ customer satisfaction survey 顧客滿意度調查
- ☐ direct marketing promotion 直銷宣傳活動
- ☐ financial risk 財務風險
- ☐ formal business attire 正式的商業服裝
- ☐ investment strategy 投資策略
- ☐ magazine subscription 雜誌訂閱
- ☐ manufacturing process 製造過程
- ☐ overseas branch office 海外分公司
- ☐ product demonstration 產品展示
- ☐ product promotion strategy 產品促銷策略
- ☐ production quota 生產量
- ☐ qualified candidate 符合資格的人選
- ☐ relative priority 相對優先權
- ☐ schedule conflict 行程撞期
- ☐ travel expenses 交通費用
- ☐ welcoming remark 歡迎詞

其他慣用語　　　　　　　　　　　　　　Track 98

☐ along with 連同	☐ it is imperative that ……是極重要的
☐ in an effort to 為……而努力	☐ no later than 不晚於……時間
☐ in keeping with 與……一致；配合	☐ on a . . . basis 以……為基準
☐ in order of 照……順序	☐ on the premise 在……前提下
☐ in preparation for 為……做準備	☐ on time 按時；準時
☐ in the event of 由於	☐ with the exception of 除……以外

Exercise

Read the text below. For each empty space in the text, select the best answer to complete the text.

Questions 1-4 *refer to the following memo.*

OFFICE MEMO

To: All employees　　　　　　　　　　　**From:** President
Subject: Promotion　　　　　　　　　　 **Date:** June 12

I am pleased to announce Craig Turner has been ---**1**--- to manager of the sales department. Beginning next Monday, all sales staff will report to Craig, who will be instituting new sales policies.

For those of you who don't know Craig, he has been with our sales department as a sales representative for five years. During that time, he has ---**2**--- had one of the best sales records.

---**3**--- joining our company, Craig was a sales representative for an electronics company. He graduated from Central College with a degree in business administration. Central College is known for producing dedicated and hard-working sales associates. ---**4**---

Yvonne Francis
President

---

1. (A) enhanced　　(B) supervised　　(C) promoted　　(D) evaluated
   Your answer: Ⓐ Ⓑ Ⓒ Ⓓ

2. (A) consistent　　(B) consistency　　(C) consistently　　(D) more consistent
   Your answer: Ⓐ Ⓑ Ⓒ Ⓓ

3. (A) Yet　　(B) But　　(C) Although　　(D) Before
   Your answer: Ⓐ Ⓑ Ⓒ Ⓓ

4. (A) Because of this, please excuse anything Craig might say.
   (B) Don't let this intimidate you, though, Craig is a reformed person.
   (C) Craig's experience in biology has proved to be invaluable.
   (D) Craig has shown time and time again that he fits this mold.
   Your answer: Ⓐ Ⓑ Ⓒ Ⓓ

Part 6 — Text Completion

Practice Test PART 6

Directions:
Read the texts that follow. A word, phrase, or sentence is missing in parts of each text. Four answer choices for each question are given below the text. Select the best answer to complete the text. Then mark the letter (A), (B), (C), or (D) on your answer sheet.

Questions 1-4 refer to the following article.

Moving to a foreign country might seem like a daunting thing to do, but thousands of people do it every day. For some, it's a lifestyle choice. Maybe the climate or working hours ---**1**--- them better. For others, it's a matter of necessity. If you have a family to support and there isn't any work in your home country, you have ---**2**--- choice but to look elsewhere. Three things that make the big move easier, according to experts, are research, family involvement, and an open mind. Your research should tell you what the job and housing markets are like, and hopefully lead to a little preparatory language learning. Family support is key to any move. ---**3**--- An open mind, of course, is necessary for when you arrive ---**4**--- you aren't overwhelmed by the new culture.

1. (A) appear
   (B) suit
   (C) seem
   (D) appeal

2. (A) many
   (B) much
   (C) little
   (D) a few

3. (A) Make sure that your loved ones know what's happening at every step.
   (B) They will tell you where to go next, so just follow their lead.
   (C) If they aren't giving you the support you need, you'll have to reconsider your vacation.
   (D) It wouldn't be wise to live in a house with unlocked doors.

4. (A) even though
   (B) so that
   (C) as though
   (D) now that

Questions 5-8 refer to the following notice.

Pemberwood County Career Fair

Pemberwood College will be holding a career fair that will be attended by a number of prestigious companies on Friday, November 18.

International companies will be attending to meet with our students, ---5--- a number of well-known local employers. The event is organized in collaboration with the town mayor and county council as part of a drive to help combat increasing youth unemployment.

Our college is a key player in these efforts and has earned a ---6--- for helping students make the right career decisions. In the last two years, we are proud to say that not one of our graduates ---7--- to find employment.

Please help us make this another successful event. We hope to continue to increase the opportunities available to our county's youngsters and allow them to showcase their talents and personal achievements. ---8---

5. (A) in order that
   (B) in brief
   (C) as long as
   (D) along with

6. (A) repute
   (B) reputable
   (C) reputation
   (D) reputed

7. (A) will fail
   (B) has failed
   (C) to fail
   (D) failing

8. (A) By building this showcase we will be able to hold nightly auditions.
   (B) The most talented child will win.
   (C) With support from the kids we will have the money in no time.
   (D) Remember, the achievements of the youth reflect on the county as a whole.

Part 6 Text Completion

Questions 9-12 refer to the following e-mail.

To: mikekeller@bestmail.com
From: jc-magritte@atheetours.com
Subject: Tour Package to France

Dear Mr. Keller,

Thank you for your interest in our tours. The tour package to France ---**9**--- you mentioned in your e-mail to us begins on the twelfth of each month, is led by an excellent tour guide, and comes with accommodation, meals, and transportation within France.

To answer your questions:
a. ---**10**--- However, we can arrange for you to be ---**11**--- at the airport and brought to your hotel if you send us your flight details.
b. You'll be staying at a five-star hotel in the center of Paris. The amenities ---**12**--- a swimming pool, sauna, gym, and a restaurant with three Michelin stars.
c. The tour includes four days in the city and six days exploring the north of France (Mont Saint Michel, Le Mans, and many more). Please check the itinerary on our website for more details.

If you have any further questions, please contact me.

Sincerely,

Jean - Claude Magritte
Athée Tours

9. (A) who (B) where
   (C) that (D) what

10. (A) The difference in price is related to the time of the year.
    (B) There are several souvenir shops in the airport
    (C) We are not affiliated with any restaurants.
    (D) I'm afraid that the price doesn't include airfare from the United States.

11. (A) found (B) greeted
    (C) discovered (D) saluted

12. (A) include (B) including
    (C) inclusion (D) inclusive

Part 7　Reading Comprehension 閱讀測驗

題型介紹

題數	五十四題（多益考試兩百題中的第 147~200 題）
題型說明	• 文章具各種題材和形式，包括廣告、書信、備忘錄、公告、即時訊息對話、表格、圖表及文章報導等。 • 分為單篇閱讀（single passages）約 10 篇文章，每篇搭配 2~4 個問題，以及雙篇和多篇閱讀 5 組文章（double/triple passages），每組搭配 5 個問題。
建議作答時間	55 分鐘（平均每題約 1 分鐘）

基本作答流程與技巧

Step 1　先讀導引句
先看開頭導引句 "Questions . . . refer to the following (article type)." 了解文章形式。

Step 2　看問題並快速瀏覽答案選項
面對大量閱讀文章與題目，有效掌控作答時間並正確快速解題乃得分關鍵。因此作答時應把重心放在「題目」，而非理解文章的全部內容。

Step 3　依問題類型決定答題順序
須了解文章整體內容的主旨題、除外題及推論題可最後作答，而僅與部分內容相關的細節題則可一邊掃描文章內容，一邊找出答案。

Step 4　快速掃瞄文章主體並尋找答案線索
平常閱讀時即應培養迅速掃描文章內容的能力，並針對題目找出答案所在，如主旨題往往在文章開頭前幾句便會出現，而細節題則從與題目相對應的人、事、時、地、物等（尤其注意相對應的名詞關鍵字詞）找出答案。

Step 5　針對各題組果斷收尾
再次強調，應考時務必掌握作答時間，每題平均約 1 分鐘（即一篇文章若有 3 題的話，該題組共可花約 3 分鐘作答）。切勿花太多時間陷在無法迅速解答的難題，導致後來驚覺時間不夠而無法完成較易得分的題目。若有未能完成作答的難題，利用最後 1 分鐘大致猜測可能的答案後，將答案卡填滿。

Part 7 Reading Comprehension

常考題型與解題技巧

題型	問題範例	解題技巧
1. 主旨題	• What is the (main) purpose of the (notice/memo/e-mail)? • Why was the (memo/letter) written? • Why did A write to B?	💡 如同聽力單元的主旨題，閱讀測驗的 main idea questions 也屬於拿分題，因為文章大意或主旨往往從整篇內容多處可找出答案，看完整篇再答即可。
2. 細節題	• What time does the (event) begin? • Where is (place) located? • How long will sth. last?	💡 這類問題占 Part 7 的多數，問法包羅萬象，但多為 Wh- questions。 💡 細節題一般會依文章順序出題。快速瀏覽問題和選項後，便馬上回文章中，試著將答案找出。
3. 同義字	• The word "..." in paragraph 3, line 5 is closest in meaning to	💡 有時一個單字可有多種意思，因此需要根據該字的前後文理解其意思，然後再從選項中找出與該意思相近的字。
4. 除外題	• What is NOT mentioned/indicated/cited ...? • What is (NOT) true of ...?	💡 要把各選項所敘述的事物全找出來，然後一一對照並找出正確或排除錯誤的選項。
5. 篇章結構題	• In which of the following positions marked [1], [2], [3], and [4] does the following sentence best belong? "..."	💡 題目會給一個新的句子，須把這個句子插入到適當的位置。須注意所插入的句子必須和前後句子在邏輯關係及脈絡上保持一致。
6. 推論題	• What can be inferred about sth./sb.? • What is suggested about sb. in the letter? • What kind of company does sb. most likely work for?	💡 題目中會出現 implied / inferred / suggested / most likely 等字眼。 💡 答案往往不會直接在文章中顯示，而是要應考者根據內文資訊，以合理邏輯的方式去判斷或推敲。
7. 整合題	• What feature do A and B have in common? • Wh- questions	💡 出現於多篇文章中，需要結合其中兩篇內容才能回答。大多整合題沒有明顯辨識之字眼或模式。若在依循某問題關鍵字閱讀其中一篇文章無法找到解答時，便須整合另一篇文章資訊方能解題。

文章類型與閱讀重點

文章類型	閱讀重點
Advertisement 廣告	• 字數通常較少，且部分或全部由不完整句子組成，內容常會包含一些零散資訊（如商品或服務項目的條列、折扣訊息、時間或地點等）。 • 題目中常會出現含 NOT 的「除外題」，因此要注意廣告中的條列項目。
Letter/E-mail 信件／電子郵件	• 先找出寫信者及收信者分別為誰。 • e-mail 要注意「subject」為何。 • 書信的開頭前幾句常會表明信件或電子郵件的主旨或目的。
Memo/Notice 備忘錄／公告	• 先閱讀開頭部分，了解其主旨或目的。 • 找出公告對象、事項內容及因應措施等訊息。
Calendar/Schedule 時程／時間表	• 注意各項活動或節目的時間、地點、活動主要內容與相關費用等。
Meeting Notice / Meeting Minutes 開會通知／會議記錄	• 留意會議的時間、地點及與會人員等基本資訊。 • 了解會議主要目的及討論的重點內容。
Form/Graph 表格／圖表	• 先查看圖表中的標題及主要項目（如 X 軸及 Y 軸各代表什麼）。 • 根據題目找出圖表所呈現的意義、差異性或關聯性。
Article 文章	• 一般報導開頭便會說明主要事件，再交代事情的發展及相關人、事、時、地、物等。雜誌文章則要留意整篇文章所要傳達的主題。 • 面對文章字數較多的內容，務必記得要針對題目找答案，並充分運用「掃瞄能力」以減少閱讀時間。
Text Message Chain 即時訊息對話	• 訊息中即使涵蓋許多不完整的句子或對話片段，仍可找出訊息所要傳達的主旨。 • 通常會有一題詢問某個時間點說的某句話是什麼意思，此時須依上下文意來判斷該句語意。

小提醒 多篇文章其實就是組合任兩篇或三篇上述文章類型。

Part 7 Reading Comprehension

常考文章類型與考題範例　廣告

Example

Questions 1-2 refer to the following advertisement.

Roomi's Electronics Shop

85 First Avenue
San Jose, California
Telephone: 408-214-9233

***

Get on down to Roomi's Electronics Shop for our going-out-of-business sale!

EVERYTHING MUST GO!

***

- Cameras down 20%
- Computers down 15%
- Appliances down as much as 40%

Store Hours:　9:00 a.m.- 10:00 p.m. Sunday-Thursday
　　　　　　　　10:00 a.m.- 11:00 p.m. Friday & Saturday

Sale ends on Saturday, October 20
Expect long queues as this is an event not to be missed.

---

1. Which item will likely be sold at the greatest discount?
   (A) Cell Phone
   (B) Computer
   (C) Microwave
   (D) Camera

2. What information does NOT appear in the advertisement?
   (A) The business hours of the store
   (B) The prices of the items on sale
   (C) The types of offerings available
   (D) The last day of the going-out-of-business sale

解析

Q1 問「哪一項商品可能提供最多折扣？」，比對答案選項和廣告內容的條列部分，選項 (C)「微波爐」屬於家電（Appliances）的一種，為各選項中折扣最多的。

Q2 為除外題，將各選項一一比對廣告內容，選項 (B)「特價品的價格」在廣告中並未提及，廣告只列出了各類商品的折扣範圍。

Exercise

Read the following passage and select the best answer for each question.

Questions 1-2 refer to the following advertisement.

Grand Opening

Jim's Sports Center will open for business on the 1st of next month. To celebrate, we are offering some great deals!

If you buy a membership during opening week, you'll get:
- 20% off a yearly membership
  OR
- 15% off a monthly membership

In addition, we are pleased to announce that on opening day, local champion runner Roy Gent will be at our store to give some training tips to all enthusiasts, young and old.

Also, come and try our heated indoor Olympic-sized swimming pool. Free for members, non-members $4.

Other facilities:
- Sauna
- Massage room
- Café
- Reading area

For more information, call 740-858-1111
Or visit us on the Web at www.jimssportscenter.com

1. How long will discounts be offered on membership purchases?
   (A) One week
   (B) Two weeks
   (C) All year
   (D) One month
   Your answer: Ⓐ Ⓑ Ⓒ Ⓓ

2. What is NOT true about Jim's Sports Center?
   (A) There is a café in the store.
   (B) A local athlete will be there opening day.
   (C) It will have its grand opening next month.
   (D) The pool will cost four dollars for everyone.
   Your answer: Ⓐ Ⓑ Ⓒ Ⓓ

常考文章類型與考題範例　書信

Example

Questions 1-2 refer to the following e-mail.

To:	robertson@hopmail.net
From:	kfisher@eisley.com
Subject:	More Information Needed

Dear Mr. Robertson,

I saw the advertisement for job code KRS-1 on your website and was hoping for some more information. A little background about myself: I have over three years' experience in the hospitality field and speak two foreign languages. I feel I would be perfect for this role. However, I think that some of the information on the website is a little vague. Is the position for the night shift? What is the salary? Do staff members receive discounts on hotel stays? I would appreciate if you could reply at your earliest convenience. Thank you.

Yours sincerely,

Karrie Fisher

1. What is the main purpose of the e-mail?
   (A) To ask for a discount at a hotel
   (B) To ask for a raise
   (C) To get more details about a job position
   (D) To thank someone after a job interview

2. What kind of job is KRS-1 most likely to be?
   (A) School teacher
   (B) IT staff
   (C) Bank clerk
   (D) Hotel receptionist

解析

Q1 為主旨題。從電子郵件的 subject 及第一句 I saw the advertisement for job . . . and was hoping for some more information. 即知答案應選 (C)，主要目的是要取得某工作職務的更多細節資訊。

Q2 題目中有 most likely 字眼，為推論題。問代號 KRS-1 有可能是哪一種工作。由寄信人提到自己在 hospitality field 有超過三年的經驗，因此非常適合該項職務，而一般 hospitality field 乃指餐飲旅館領域的相關服務業；另一線索則是信中問到員工入住飯店是否享有折扣。故答案選 (D)「飯店櫃台接待人員」。

Exercise

Read the following passage and select the best answer for each question.

Questions 1-2 refer to the following letter.

Evergreen Apartment Management Committee

155 Park Avenue
Orlando, FL 33429
Telephone: 407-551-4826

Dear Evergreen Apartment Residents:

I'm sure that you have noticed recently that there have been a few problems with the water and, to a lesser extent, the gas supply. We assure you that we are doing our utmost to get these issues sorted out.

We first noticed the water problem when Mr. Cash of Apartment 72 complained that his water bill had increased by a significant amount. As he had been surfing in Maui, he realized that he could not have used so much.

After talking with Mr. Cash, we discovered the problem was not localized to his apartment, and we have decided to change the plumbing throughout the whole building. This will be a major renovation, so we ask that you bear with us, and we apologize in advance. If any other residents have noticed irregular bills, please contact Carla Tangoh at the Russell Water Company by phone at (212)-543-9023 or e-mail ctangoh@russellwater.com to organize a refund on your bill.

Thank you,

Trent Blues

1. What is the main purpose of the letter?
   (A) To explain where Mr. Cash has been recently
   (B) To give information about issues in the building
   (C) To tell people how to get a discount on their utilities
   (D) To introduce the new management team
   Your answer: Ⓐ Ⓑ Ⓒ Ⓓ

2. In what situation should the residents contact Carla Tangoh?
   (A) If they want their plumbing changed
   (B) If they'll be on vacation during the renovations
   (C) If the water or gas isn't working in their apartments
   (D) If their water bill seems unusually high
   Your answer: Ⓐ Ⓑ Ⓒ Ⓓ

常考文章類型與考題範例　即時訊息對話

Example

Questions 1-2 refer to the following text message chain.

Alex Kreischer	4:45 p.m.
Jamie, have you left the office yet?	
Jamie Woodard	5:15 p.m.
Yea, why?	
Alex Kreischer	5:16 p.m.
Oh, I need the key to the storage closet. I'm still churning out a few summarized reports for the shareholders and we ran out of printer paper.	
amie Woodard	5:19 p.m.
Oh, I have a spare key in the top drawer of my desk. How much longer do you think you need to work on them?	
Alex Kreischer	5:26 p.m.
An hour. Maybe two.	
Jamie Woodard	5:30 p.m.
You don't have to worry about finishing them tonight. You can do it in the morning.	
Alex Kreischer	5:32 p.m.
I don't mind. See you tomorrow!	

1. Which of the following is NOT relevant to the text massage?
   (A) An office phone　(B) A storage space
   (C) A key　(D) Sheets of blank paper

2. At 5:32 p.m., what does Mr. Kreischer mean when he writes, "I don't mind"?
   (A) He isn't really sure how long the job will take.
   (B) He'll stay and finish the reports.
   (C) He hadn't considered the woman's suggestion.
   (D) He'll do the job in the morning.

解析

Q1 為除外題，詢問何者是與簡訊無關的內容。由簡訊中 Oh, I need the key to the storage closet . . . printer paper. 得知選項 (B)、(C)、(D) 皆與本對話有關，唯選項 (A) 並未出現在簡訊內容中。

Q2 本題問克力斯裘先生寫 I don't mind. 為何意。在此上一句傑米‧屋德說他可以明天早上再完成報告，而克力斯裘先生接著說 I don't mind. 即是表達他不介意加班完成報告，故答案為 (B)。

Exercise

Read the following passage and select the best answer for each question.

Questions 1-2 refer to the following text message chain.

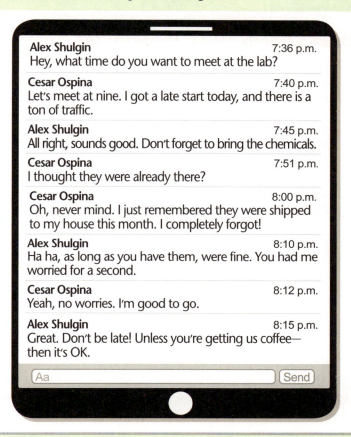

1. What is the most likely profession of the two men?
   (A) Scientists
   (B) Athletes
   (C) Chefs
   (D) Mechanics

   Your answer: Ⓐ Ⓑ Ⓒ Ⓓ

2. At 8:12, what does Mr. Ospina most likely mean when he writes, "good to go"?
   (A) He has already picked up the coffee.
   (B) He is adequately prepared to leave.
   (C) He is happy he is leaving.
   (D) He wants Mr. Shulgin to leave.

   Your answer: Ⓐ Ⓑ Ⓒ Ⓓ

Part 7 Reading Comprehension

常考文章類型與考題範例　雙篇文章

Questions 1-5 refer to the following business proposal and e-mail message.

Mackem's International Property Inc.

We are a successful property development company founded in 1975 with offices all over the world, and we are now looking for a partner firm to take over our Home Maintenance and Gardens Department.

We have some very important clients, including famous celebrities, leading hotels, and major corporations, who expect the quality associated with Mackem's. If your company would like to be part of the family, your application needs to show the following:

i. References demonstrating your company's relevant experience and abilities in the home maintenance field

ii. A clear system of organization within your company

iii. A strong commitment to service, including detailed statements about how you would approach our clients

More requirements will be explained in later e-mails if we feel your initial proposals are strong enough. Only serious applicants need apply.

Ref No: E-40
E-mail: jeffwilliams@mackems.net

To:	jeffwilliams@mackems.net
From:	royfrancis@baggies.com
Subject:	Re: your proposal

Dear Mr. Williams,

I would like you to consider Ace HomeCare Maintenance Services to lead your Home Maintenance and Gardens Department. Our company has been around for over 15 years and maintains a large presence across Australia. We are known for our vast experience in home maintenance and the superior service we give to all our customers. And we have references from our clientele to prove it. Attached are a copy of our organizational structure, a detailed company statement, and several letters from our clients.

We are confident we have what it takes to be the perfect partner for Mackem's, and we are hoping for a swift reply.

Yours sincerely,

Roy Francis
Vice President, Ace HomeCare Maintenance Services

1. What is the main purpose of Mackem's business proposal?
   (A) To explain why Ace HomeCare should partner with Mackem's
   (B) To interest another company in buying Macken's assets
   (C) To find another company to take over a portion of its business
   (D) To find someone to join Mackem's management team

2. According to the proposal, which of these is NOT mentioned as one of Mackem's types of customers?
   (A) Famous people   (B) Big companies
   (C) Hotels   (D) Sports centers

3. In the e-mail message, the word "presence" in paragraph 1, line 3 is closest in meaning to
   (A) nearness   (B) existence
   (C) personality   (D) spirit

4. Why is Roy Francis contacting Jeff Williams?
   (A) To announce his company's interest in Mackem's business proposal
   (B) To inform him that his company doesn't want to make a deal
   (C) To say that he will be opening his own company
   (D) To explain why he doesn't have reference letters yet

5. What do the two companies have in common?
   (A) They both only operate in Australia.
   (B) They both are more than a decade old.
   (C) They are owned by the same person.
   (D) They have the same name.

解析

Q1 主旨題，問麥肯斯公司商業提案的主要目的。由提案第一段後半句提到 . . . we are now looking for a partner firm to take over our Home Maintenance and Gardens Department. 「我們此刻正在尋找夥人接收我們的房屋維護及花園部門」可知答案選 (C)。

Q2 為除外題，問何者「不是」麥肯斯公司的客戶類別。比對提案第二段中 We have some very important clients, including famous celebrities, leading hotels, and major corporations . . . 即知文中並未提到選項 (D)「運動中心」。

Q3 這裡考同義字。電子郵件中第一段第三行 maintains a large presence across Australia「在全澳洲擁有高能見度」，presence 在此指「在場；存在」，意近選項中的 (B) existence。

Q4 問 Roy Francis 為何寫信給 Jeff Williams，由電子郵件開頭 I would like you to consider . . . to lead your Home Maintenance and Gardens Department.「希望您考慮……帶領貴公司的房屋維護和花園部門」及最後一段 We are confident we have what it takes to be the perfect partner for Mackem's . . . 「我們自信擁有成為麥肯斯完美夥伴的一切條件……」，可知答案選 (A)。

Q5 此為整合題，問兩公司的共通點。從各選項答案比對內文一一檢視，選項 (A)：由提案中可知麥肯斯公司在全球都有辦事處，並非只在澳洲營運，故不對；選項 (B)：decade 指「十年」，由第一篇文章可知麥肯斯公司創立於 1975 年，第二篇文章則提到艾司房屋營運超過 15 年，故選項 (B)「兩家公司皆超過十年」為正確答案。

常考文章類型與考題範例　多篇文章

Questions 1-5 refer to the following letter, invoice, and e-mail.

Dear Miss Harding,

You are receiving this letter because our records indicate you may have purchased a product now identified as defective. Your purchase may qualify you for a full refund or replacement. Please read below to learn how to apply for your refund or replacement.

Item(s):

- HomeHeat 7500 Ceramic Tower Heater

If you purchased the above item(s) between the dates of October 1– April 30, and the serial number does not exceed HH75005000, please bring the below confirmation number, proof of purchase and the item in question to your local retailer for a refund or replacement.

Confirmation number: 1810141536SRSPN

Defects: Product's safety mechanism defective; item may overheat, potential fire hazard.

Once your item is confirmed as defective, you will be issued a refund or replacement.

Best,

HomeHeat Customer Service

Receipt 000459685

Wilson Electronics
2401 Upper Midlands Rd
Pittsburg, PA 15214
412-775-9003
Purchase date: October 14, 15:36 pm
Payment method: Credit card (-XX97, exp. 2025)

Item	Unit cost	Volume	Amount
HomeHeat 7500 Ceramic Tower Heater (serial #HH75008015)	$59.99	1	$59.99
LED Flashlight	$45.98	2	$91.96
Subtotal			$151.95
Sales Tax (7%)			$10.63
Total			$162.58

To: HomeHeat Customer Service (service@homeheat.ca)
From: Jane Harding (j.harding@weblink.com)
Subject: Defective product

Dear Sir or Madam:

I am sending this e-mail to inquire regarding the product I purchased on October 14. I understand there may be some danger from using this product, but it is currently the only heater I own, and I have used it without issue so far. I have tried calling the customer service line but waited too long or was transferred mid-conversation. I would like to know how long the replacement process takes, as I am worried the store doesn't have these items in stock. It's getting very cold here, and if the item needs to be replaced, I would like to do so ASAP, but I can't go without a heater. Please advise at your earliest convenience. I have attached an image of my receipt.

Thank you.

Jane Harding

1. Why is Miss Harding returning the product she bought?
   (A) It is not bright enough.
   (B) It may start a fire.
   (C) It doesn't get hot enough.
   (D) She wants a different model.

2. Why is Miss Harding writing this e-mail?
   (A) She doesn't know where to return the item.
   (B) She wants to know if she can keep using it.
   (C) She doesn't know how to return the item.
   (D) She wants to know how long she will have to wait for a new one.

解析

Q1 此為細節題，詢問哈汀小姐要退貨的原因。由第一封信件說 . . . item may overheat, potential fire hazard.「品項會過熱，可能會有引燃的危險」得知她被告知此產品可能會有引燃的問題，故正確答案為 **(B)**。

Q2 問哈汀小姐寫電子郵件的原因，由關鍵句 I would like to know how long the replacement process takes . . .「我想知道換貨的流程需要多久……」可知她想知道換貨後多久可以收到新的產品，故答案選 **(D)**。

3. Which item does the customer NOT need to bring in to get her refund or replacement?
   (A) Credit card
   (B) Confirmation number
   (C) Receipt
   (D) The defective item

4. What will be the most likely response to this customer's e-mail?
   (A) She should replace her product as soon as possible.
   (B) She must first contact customer service.
   (C) Her item is not defective.
   (D) The item isn't in stock.

5. What is the most likely reason Miss Harding might not get a refund?
   (A) She bought the item outside the required period.
   (B) She doesn't have a receipt for her purchase.
   (C) The problem with the product has been resolved.
   (D) The serial number does not qualify.

Q3 為除外題,詢問什麼是退費或是換貨不需要提供的,可以由第一篇當中... please bring the below confirmation number, proof of purchase and the item in question to your local retailer for a refund or replacement.「……請攜帶以下認證號碼、購買證明以及有問題的產品到您當地的零售商尋求退費或是換貨。」即知並未提到選項 (A)「信用卡」。

Q4 本題詢問商家可能會如何回覆這封顧客的電子郵件。由顧客的電子郵件中提及... and I have used it without issue so far.「……目前為止使用上都沒有問題。」以及看其附件的流水編號並不符合退換貨規定,可以推測她購買的產品並沒有瑕疵故障的問題,故正確答案為 (C)。

Q5 此為整合題,問哈汀小姐可能無法退費的原因。由第一封電子郵件中... and the serial number does not exceed HH75005000「……並且流水編號小於 HH75005000」,及收據上的流水編號為 HH75008015 得知她購買的產品流水編號並不符合退費的規定,故答案應選 (D)。

(A) 由收據中得知哈汀小姐於十月十四日購買商品,符合十月一日到四月三十日之間購買的規定。

(B) 哈汀小姐的電子郵件中有附上收據。

(C) 文中並未提到產品問題已獲得解決。

Practice Test PART 7

Directions:
In this part you will read a selection of texts, such as magazine and newspaper articles, e-mails, and instant messages. Each text or set of texts is followed by several questions. Select the best answer for each question and mark the letter (A), (B), (C), or (D) on your answer sheet.

Questions 1-2 refer to the following advertisement.

Coming Soon

Paul Brown's Café

The newest location of Paul Brown's Café will open at this spot on February 21, bringing to the area the best in fine dining. Paul Brown's offers an array of international flavors ranging from Italian to Spanish to French.

Of course, Paul Brown's is best known for its excellent steaks. All steaks are grilled to perfection over a charcoal fire and flavored with spices from Spain and Italy or wine sauces from France.

Our all-you-can-eat buffet offers:
- roast beef
- turkey
- fruit and salad bar
- dessert and drinks

Be sure to come for our Grand Opening weekend February 21-22, during which time all customers will receive a complimentary dessert with their meals.

1. What do most people know about the Paul Brown's Café?
   (A) It has Italian food.
   (B) It has Spanish food.
   (C) It serves fine steaks.
   (D) It has a salad bar.

2. Which of the following foods might you get for free at the restaurant during its opening week?
   (A) Steak
   (B) Salad
   (C) Roast beef
   (D) Dessert

Questions 3-4 refer to the following text message chain.

3. Why is Sam Hall sending this message?
   (A) He won't be able to make it to the meeting.
   (B) He will arrive late to the meeting.
   (C) He hasn't finished the presentation.
   (D) He will need to leave the meeting early.

4. At 11:35 a.m., what does Sam Hall imply when he writes, "keep your cool"?
   (A) Craig shouldn't let anyone know he is angry.
   (B) There's no reason for Craig to be nervous.
   (C) Craig is sometimes impatient.
   (D) He doesn't think Craig is capable of conducting the meeting.

Questions 5-7 refer to the following e-mail.

From:	Margaret Schumacher
To:	All employees
Subject:	New attendance rules

Hello everyone,

This is Schumacher from Human Resources with a message about a change of company policy concerning attendance and clocking in/out.

As our business has grown, our employee pool has expanded considerably. We started out with a staff of 25, including one person who was in control of all human-resource and accounting issues. We now have over 2,000 employees and 20 full-time administrative staff. In order to reduce waste and improve efficiency, we have decided to switch to an entirely electronic system for clocking in and out, applying for sick leave, and making personal leave requests.

Your new electronic swipe cards should have already been given to you, and you should begin using them on Monday morning. Each manager will be responsible for using the reporting system accessible on the internal network when approving sick days after his or her employees have returned to work and recorded their absences. Vacation leave and casual leave will be booked in advance by the employee with the relevant manager, who will use the same system to register it.

Thank you for your cooperation,

Margaret Schumacher
Human Resources

5. What is the main point of this e-mail?
   (A) The company's vacation allowance has changed.
   (B) The company is expanding quickly.
   (C) The company is implementing a new system.
   (D) The company is hiring extra managers.

6. What is the purpose of moving to an electronic system?
   (A) To make the computer system more user-friendly
   (B) To save company resources
   (C) To give more vacation time
   (D) To give more responsibility to managers

7. Which of these is true of the new cards?
   (A) They will be distributed on Monday.
   (B) They have been distributed already.
   (C) They can be found on the internal system.
   (D) They must be turned in to HR.

Part 7 Reading Comprehension

Questions 8-11 refer to the following employee notice.

The first annual staff training session for Perseus Inc. will take place on the 15th of next month. The training will focus on the new office management software and the new quality control guidelines for production. All office employees, members of management, and quality control officers are required to attend. Attendance is optional for workers on the factory floor.
—[1]—

The details are as follows:
Title: "Office Management and Quality Control"
Date: August 15th
Times: 10 a.m. – 5 p.m.
Location: Conference Room A

The training will consist of a briefing on each topic, a question and answer session, and a practical exercise. Lunch and refreshments will be provided. All attendees will be paid at their regular daily rate.

—[2]— As you may have heard, we'll be switching over to the new office management software in September and implementing the new quality control guidelines in October. —[3]—

If for any reason you will be unable to attend, or if you have any questions about the training session, please contact the personnel department at extension 187.
—[4]—

8. What is the purpose of the notice?
    (A) To explain what each department's training program entails
    (B) To give information about an upcoming training session
    (C) To request that people attend an optional training session
    (D) To outline the training schedule for the rest of the year

9. Which group of people must attend the training?
    (A) Factory floor workers
    (B) Managers
    (C) Cafeteria workers
    (D) Outside contractors

10. What should an employee who will be on vacation on August 15th do?
    (A) Cancel the trip
    (B) Tell personnel 187 days in advance
    (C) Submit their training questions in writing
    (D) Contact personnel by phone

11. In which of the following positions marked [1], [2], [3], and [4] does the following sentence best belong?
    "Further details on both changes will be circulated by e-mail."
    (A) [1]
    (B) [2]
    (C) [3]
    (D) [4]

Questions 12-15 refer to the following survey results.

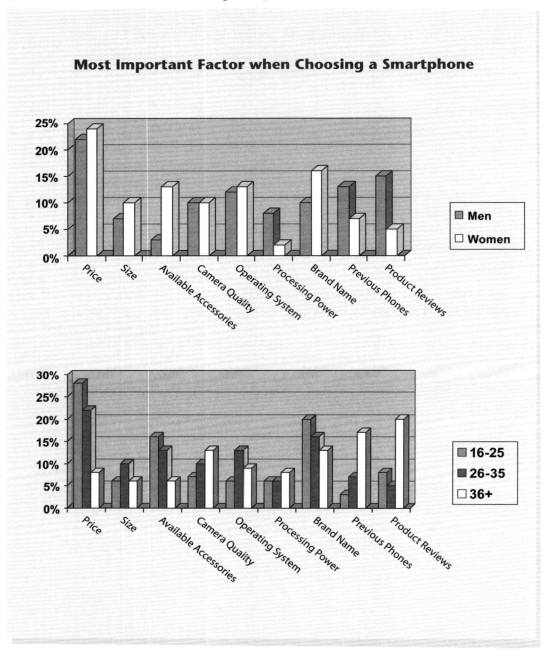

Source: Everyday Tech, a technology news site. Consumers were questioned about their main considerations before purchasing their next smartphone. Each person's top answer was recorded. The survey was conducted inside an electronics store among men and women over the age of 16 who were there to purchase a new smartphone. Participants received no discount or compensation.

12. Which smartphone feature did an equal percentage of men and women say was the most important?
    (A) The operating system used on the phone
    (B) The phone's processing power
    (C) The quality of the phone's camera
    (D) The size of the phone

13. Which group of consumers was most concerned with the brand of smartphone they would buy?
    (A) Young adults
    (B) Men
    (C) People over the age of 36
    (D) Everyone was equally concerned

14. What can be inferred about smartphone product reviews?
    (A) A large percentage of women rely on reviews for making purchasing decisions.
    (B) No one pays attention to which smartphones critics prefer.
    (C) Teenagers have no interest in reading reviews of products.
    (D) Men over the age of 36 value the information in them.

15. Based on the information from the survey, what smartphone feature should be highlighted in advertisements to attract the most consumers?
    (A) Size
    (B) Price
    (C) Accessories
    (D) Processing Power

Part 7 Reading Comprehension

Questions 16-18 refer to the minutes of a meeting.

Meeting Minutes

Present: Colonel Henry Waff, Councilor Cliff Bass, Norma Weiss, Gladys Ong, and Jamal Iqbal
Subject: Plans for New Children's Fun Center

9 a.m.	Meeting called to order and those present sign register.
9:15 a.m.	Cliff Bass outlines rough draft of proposals for the Newbridge site, which Norma Weiss claims to be too ambitious.
9:20 a.m.	Cliff agrees that the inclusion of a swimming pool may be costly, but Jamal Iqbal points out that this could have benefits for the fitness levels of local people of all ages. All agree.
9:30 a.m.	Henry Waff agrees that in order to be cost effective, it should be inclusive of all and not just focus on children. He says he would prefer it to be a community center which also offers night time classes.
9:45 a.m.	Cliff agrees to amend proposals and create another plan for the next meeting which is due to be held on December 5.
9:50 a.m.	Meeting ends with all present at the meeting reaching a consensus.

16. How long was the meeting?
    (A) 30 minutes
    (B) Nearly one hour
    (C) About two hours
    (D) Several hours

17. Which of the following people did NOT make any comments during the meeting?
    (A) Cliff Bass
    (B) Henry Waff
    (C) Jamal Iqbal
    (D) Gladys Ong

18. What will happen at the next meeting?
    (A) The council will look over a new plan.
    (B) They will pick classes for the community center.
    (C) The original plan will be discussed more.
    (D) A new head councilor will be chosen.

Questions 19-21 refer to the following letter.

DetSoft Systems
150 Court Street
Newark, NJ 14513
Telephone: 1-212-555-8111

Dear Mr. Adams,

Thanks for taking the time to meet with me while I was in Seattle. I had a great time while I was there, and I even got to play a few rounds of golf, which I don't usually have time for when I'm here in Milan. Thanks also for introducing me to your technical manager, Mr. Kent.

After speaking with you and Mr. Kent at our meeting, I feel that my company has a lot to offer Advanced Tech. The problem that you mentioned having with maintaining your databases is interesting. One of our strengths here at DetSoft is building user-maintainable systems so that you never need to hire in external talent again. We would both design the maintenance systems and train your staff to use them, which means that you could do everything in-house. We'd also include a support and troubleshooting package that would extend for six months after the initial installation. We have found in the past that clients rarely feel the need to use it, but it's nice to have for peace of mind.

When I spoke to Mr. Kent again later, we went over some of the technical details, but to get a more accurate estimate of the work involved, we'll need to gather more information on your existing system. Let me know if you're interested, then we could start putting it all together and get a quote to you in a week or so.

Sincerely,

Bob Frankston
Bob Frankston
DetSoft Systems

19. How would DetSoft's solution be helpful to Advanced Tech?
    (A) Advanced Tech would no longer have to use databases.
    (B) The staff at Advanced Tech could maintain the company's systems.
    (C) Advanced Tech would get free support for a year.
    (D) The internal database managers at Advanced Tech could be fired.

20. The word "extend" in paragraph 2, line 7 is closest in meaning to
    (A) strain
    (B) increase
    (C) continue
    (D) include

21. What can be inferred from the letter?
    (A) DetSoft has already been hired by Advanced Tech.
    (B) Bob Frankston has all the information he needs.
    (C) The system will take a long time to perfect.
    (D) The companies have not yet reached a deal.

Part 7 Reading Comprehension

Questions 22-23 refer to the following book review.

Book review: "Chandra's Wish" by Ake Umfolosi
Reviewed by Peter Canasta, literary critic

Two words: a revelation! There are times in your life when you see or read somebody's debut, and you just know that person is going to go far. The premise of this book is very simple. Chandra is an energetic young orphan growing up in a landlocked African country, and her only dream is to waltz on the deck of a schooner she saw in a picture in a library book. There are two problems, though. One, her country is ravaged by war. And two, she doesn't know how to dance. Enter Mr. Calypso, an intriguing dance teacher with a mysterious past.

Ake draws on his own experiences growing up in an impoverished environment, and his characters often seem a little too real. This is a truly amazing debut with very memorable twists and turns. Although written for the teen market, it is highly recommended for young and old alike. More please, Ake!

22. What is true about Ake Umfolosi?
    (A) This is the second book he has written.
    (B) He works as a literary critic.
    (C) He is planning a series about Chandra.
    (D) He comes from a poor background.

23. What word best describes Peter Canasta's opinion of the book?
    (A) Predictable
    (B) Impressive
    (C) Humorous
    (D) Confusing

Questions 24-26 refer to the following article.

> In Britain, sales of bottled water have been on the increase for decades. This prompted an investigation by the government to see whether bottled water was a worthwhile purchase. —[1]—
>
> It is estimated that in some parts of London a bottle of water may cost £4, whereas the same amount of water (some 250ml) from a tap would cost less than a penny. —[2]— According to the government's report, over 95% of the money earned by bottled water companies is spent on things other than the water that is being drunk, such as advertising.
>
> Companies that sell bottled water claim their products have a number of benefits, such as containing fewer dangerous metals as their water does not run through areas exposed to metal corrosion. —[3]— However, environmental groups say these benefits pale in significance to the impact that plastic bottles have on the environment.
>
> The full findings of the report are due to be published in September, and water companies are waiting with interest as to what those findings are.
> —[4]—

24. What would be a good title for this article?
    (A) Rain, Rain Go Away
    (B) Sales of Water Reach Record High
    (C) Bottled vs. Tap Water
    (D) The Benefits of Drinking More Water

25. In which of the following positions marked [1], [2], [3], and [4] does the following sentence best belong?
    "That's 400 times more for a bottle than a glass from the faucet."
    (A) [1]
    (B) [2]
    (C) [3]
    (D) [4]

26. What do environmental groups think about plastic bottles?
    (A) They keep water away from dangerous substances.
    (B) They are more expensive than glass ones.
    (C) They are an environmentally-friendly option.
    (D) They have negative impacts on the environment.

Questions 27-29 refer to the following online chat discussion.

Libby [22:01]:
Does anyone else have a bad feeling about the vendor Hapley that Arnold decided on? I'm a little nervous about their assertions.

Jose [22:03]:
What do you mean? Their website says they've been in operation for like fifteen years, and they've won some superior business awards. They look pretty solid. Arnold used to work for them, actually.

Libby [22:04]:
I know all that, but I called some of their former clients. Didn't tell them where I was from.

Jose [22:07]:
Did you call the Anders place? They're huge.

Tetsu [22:08]:
Yeah, probably the biggest Hapley ever worked with. We can only dream of getting that big.

Libby [22:09]:
I did. We need 750k units/mo. Who remembers what the Hapley reps said in their first meeting with us? What did they say they could do?

Jose [22:13]:
Something like 1.5 mil processors/mo for six months straight. We don't need anything like that kind of volume though.

Libby [22:14]:
Well, Anders & Co. says their contract last year was for only 600k units per month for four months, and Hapley delivered late for all but one of those months. We can't operate that way. Do you guys think I should bring it up with him?

Tetsu [22:17]:
Well, you'll have to make that call, and soon. But Arnold might not be so pleased you went behind his back about it.

Jose [22:20]:
If Arnold says to trust them, I take them at their word. But in the end, you'll be taking the fall if our production runs behind schedule. Think about it, Lib.

27. Why is Libby worried about the new vendor?
    (A) She doesn't like Arnold.
    (B) She doesn't want to hire a vendor with such high volume.
    (C) She's heard they have a reputation of poor quality products.
    (D) She doesn't think they're capable of meeting production demands.

28. How does Jose feel about the vendor?
    (A) He thinks they are lucky that Arnold works for them.
    (B) He thinks they are capable of delivering the needed parts.
    (C) He likes them because he used to work there.
    (D) He thinks they are lying about their operations.

29. At [22:17], what does Tetsu imply when he writes, "make that call"?
    (A) Libby is ultimately responsible for the vendor's affect on the project.
    (B) Libby should consider speaking to Arnold about the choice of vendors.
    (C) Tetsu thinks Libby should confront the vendor about their claims.
    (D) Tetsu thinks the vendor is a good choice.

Part 7 Reading Comprehension

Questions 30-34 refer to the following job advertisement and e-mail response.

Job Ref: JC001

Your task will be to change our underperforming team into a group of real high-fliers. This is an exciting opportunity for anyone who wishes to form key relationships with debt relief organizations and big businesses at the grassroots level.

Everybody who is affected by the sudden loss of income requires understanding and motivation. The ideal candidate for this position will have a proven track record as a team leader as well as excellent listening and counseling skills and over three years' experience in a similar role. You will need to develop new strategies to improve our client repayment rates and also recruit new people to work as mediators between those who are having difficulties with their debt and their creditors.

We offer a range of benefits including:
- gym membership
- free child care
- travel allowance

Are you ready to join us? Please quote the job ref when applying.

E-mail: recruitment@debtphree.org

To:	recruitment@debtphree.org
From:	ASnow@Tydfil.com
Subject:	Re: Job Ref JC001

Dear Sir or Madam,

I am incredibly interested in this position. I have over five years' experience in a similar role and feel this challenge is just what I am looking for. I have enclosed a copy of my résumé in the hope that you will consider me for this position.

Thank you for your time.

Sincerely,

Adam Snow

30. Which field is this job opening in?
    (A) IT
    (B) Arts
    (C) Finance
    (D) Housing

31. According to the advertisement, what is the problem with the team at the moment?
    (A) They are all new employees.
    (B) They are not performing well.
    (C) They are not paying their debts.
    (D) They are collecting too much money.

32. Which of the following skills is NOT mentioned as a requirement for the position?
    (A) Sales
    (B) Counseling
    (C) Listening
    (D) Leadership

33. How much experience does Adam have?
    (A) Three years
    (B) Four years
    (C) Five years
    (D) Ten years

34. What has Adam sent with his e-mail?
    (A) Information about his job history
    (B) Photos of himself
    (C) His college transcripts
    (D) A letter of reference

Questions 35-39 refer to the following events calendar listing and e-mail inquiry.

Casey Advertising: Advertising for Small Businesses

This workshop will teach small-business owners and marketers how to use the Internet and social media to promote their businesses. These days, the Internet offers not only opportunities but also pitfalls, as unhappy customers are quick to post bad reviews when something goes wrong. So learn how to use and how to monitor websites such as Facebook, Yelp, and Google Local to make sure your business is getting the most out of the Internet.

Location: Kramer Hotel, 202 Fourth St., Oakland
Time and Date: Feb. 22, noon to 2 p.m.
Keynote Speaker: Mr. Steven Turner, entrepreneur and owner of France's Finest Coffee and Tea Story House
Admission Fee: $45

E-mail Janet at janet@caseyadagency.com or call 510-555-9931 to register.

From: Dan Cole
To: janet@caseyadagency.com
Subject: Workshop

Dear Janet,

I am interested in attending your workshop on how to use the Internet to promote my business. I recently opened an Italian restaurant, and I see a great need to improve my business's presence online. As a restaurant owner, I am particularly concerned about receiving negative reviews on popular websites. I am also wondering if I might be able to speak personally with the speaker after the workshop to ask a few questions specifically about promoting restaurants.

Thanks,

Dan Cole

35. Which of the following businesses would the workshop probably be good for?
    (A) An auto manufacturer
    (B) A gift shop
    (C) An oil company
    (D) An airline

36. What is something people will learn from the workshop?
    (A) How to post reviews
    (B) How to monitor websites
    (C) How to open a business
    (D) How to teach marketing

37. What does Dan Cole mention he is worried about?
    (A) The expense of advertising
    (B) Opening a new business
    (C) People writing bad reviews
    (D) Competition in the area

38. Why does Dan Cole want to meet with the speaker alone?
    (A) To talk about issues related to his business
    (B) To get tips on how to post better reviews
    (C) To better understand the costs of opening a coffee shop
    (D) To learn how to create a website

39. What do Steven Turner and Dan Cole have in common?
    (A) They write reviews on the same websites.
    (B) They both run coffee shops.
    (C) They are both business owners.
    (D) They are going to be guest speakers.

Part 7 Reading Comprehension

Questions 40-44 refer to the following memo, note, and profile.

Memorandum to Staff at Roman Industries

Please make our new sales manager, Omar Khan, feel at home. We have been looking for someone with Omar's skills for quite some time, and after a lot of false starts, we have finally found the best man for the job. Omar has a background in shipping in his native Dubai, which, as I'm sure you all know, is the new crossroads between East and West. As we are trying to increase our market share in the Middle East region in general, we can see that Mr. Khan's expertise will be a great asset.

He would like it to be known that he speaks English, Arabic, and French at a native level, as well as a little German. He was educated at Harvard and also spent time in Switzerland and Canada. If you have anything you would like to discuss with Omar, please feel free to knock on his door. He will be happy to answer any questions you may have.

Thanks,

Bruce Sionis

Note from Omar Khan

Thank you for the introduction, Bruce. I would like to add a bit to it and make a few things clear from the get-go, just so that we can make the transition as smooth as possible. In my previous company, I had the reputation of being great at troubleshooting. I am well versed in areas such as sales, cross-cultural communication, and so on, so I am happy to aid anyone who needs help solving a problem. But I must add that I am not afraid of letting people go if I don't feel they are pulling their own weight.

I am pleased to be taking on this new challenge and hope to make Roman Industries the top freight distribution company in the Middle East. I am very happy to be a part of the Roman family.

Best Regards,

Omar Khan

Omar Khan's Professional Networking Profile

Education
Harvard University, Bachelor of Liberal Art, Class of 2009

Experience
- Old Castle LLC, sales consultant, 2014-2017, Bern, Switzerland
- Damsal Hendi Enterprises, shipping manager, 2011-2014, Dubai, UAE
- Crane Expositions, sales representative, 2009–2011, Prague, Czech Republic

40. Why was the memo written?
    (A) To ask for applications for a position
    (B) To announce the start of a new employee
    (C) To explain why it took a long time to fill a position
    (D) To introduce the new owner of a company

41. In the memo, the word "asset" in the last line of first paragraph, is closest in meaning to
    (A) burden
    (B) property
    (C) benefit
    (D) kindness

42. According to the memo, which of the following is NOT true about Mr. Khan?
    (A) He went to college in the U.S.
    (B) He has worked in the Middle East before.
    (C) He can speak several languages.
    (D) He worked as a salesman in Canada.

43. What can be inferred about Omar Khan from his note?
    (A) He is nervous about taking on a lot of responsibility.
    (B) He thinks people who aren't capable should lose their jobs.
    (C) He prefers communicating in languages other than English.
    (D) He doesn't think the company will do well in the Middle East.

44. Which part of Omar Khan's profile is not referenced by Bruce?
    (A) The place Mr. Khan lived while working at Old Castle LLC
    (B) The school Mr. Khan graduated from in 2009
    (C) The experience Mr. Khan gained from working at Damsal Hendi
    (D) The experience Mr. Khan gained from working at Crane Expositions

Questions 45-49 refer to the following advertisement, e-mail, and response.

For Rent

A tidy workspace in a contemporary business center in bustling Trenton is available for rent. The property is surrounded by a vast assortment of magnificent shops, bars, and restaurants to enjoy and explore. The famous Pallister Theater and McClair Gallery are both only five minutes away on foot.

The interior has been renovated to the highest standard, and many of the rooms have kept their original features. All rooms benefit from lots of natural light.

Conveniently located just 10 minutes walk from the train station, with easy access to Marley and Barett.

Reference #: 57738
Call 0800-482-6464
Or e-mail Mike Pheelan: mpheelan@trenchtonproperties.com

To:	mpheelan@trenchtonproperties.com
From:	kdickson@quickmail.com
Subject:	Ref number 57738

Dear Mr. Pheelan,

I am e-mailing to ask about the possibility of viewing the property at the above reference number, as it seems to be just what I am looking for. I have a number of enquiries which I will raise with you when we meet, but for now I'd like to know what the monthly rental fee is. I'm also interested in what other companies operate from the same building.

I'd like to see the place either on the 27th or as soon as possible after that date.

Regards,

Kerry Dickson

To:	kdickson@quickmail.com
From:	mpheelan@trenchtonproperties.com
Subject:	Re: Ref number 57738

Dear Kerry Dickson,

The space you are asking about has already been claimed. However there are two spaces in the same building matching the same description—just on different floors. Space A (5th floor) will have an invitation-only preview on the 26th, then open up for public viewing on the 28th. Space B (12th floor) will have an invitation-only preview on the 29th, then open up for public viewing on the 30th. I'd be delighted to extend you an invitation to either one of the previews. The space rents for $3000–$4000, depending on the floor.

Regards,

Mike Pheelan

45. What is the advertisement for?
    (A) A home
    (B) A restaurant
    (C) A school
    (D) An office

46. How far away is the theater from the property for rent?
    (A) 10 minutes from the train station
    (B) A five-minute walk
    (C) 15 minutes by car
    (D) Next to the gallery

47. What is NOT mentioned about the rooms in the advertisement?
    (A) They've been renovated.
    (B) They are air conditioned.
    (C) They still have some original features.
    (D) They are very bright.

48. What can be assumed about Marley and Barett?
    (A) They are the owners of the property.
    (B) They are products sold at the nearby shops.
    (C) They are applicants interested in the property.
    (D) They are neighboring towns.

49. Based on the e-mails, on which date will Kerry Dickson likely visit the property?
    (A) 26th
    (B) 27th
    (C) 28th
    (D) 29th

Part 7 Reading Comprehension

Questions 50-54 refer to the following advertisement, online ticketing website, and e-mail.

Serendipity Travel Agency is much more than a website to book airline tickets. Our agency handles your vacation experience from start to finish. Once you decide where you would like to travel to, simply select the days/times that work for you to travel and we will book the tickets for you. After this has been completed, one of our service representatives will contact you via e-mail to discuss possible ideas for your vacation.

Would you like to relax on a beach and enjoy the stars, or are you possibly more interested in getting out and trekking through a new part of the world? Our service representatives are standing by ready to help tailor a personalized vacation experience unlike any other.

Welcome to Serendipity Travel Agency. Your journey starts here.

(Please note that because we are not an airline company, no alterations can be made.)

Airline	Flight Details	Duration	Price
Airflow Airlines	**Taipei → Tokyo** Dec. 15th 8:00 a.m.	3h20m	$200.00
Airflow Airlines	**Tokyo → Buenos Aires** Jan. 7th 11:55 p.m.	26h10m	$1,355.00
Western United Air/ Kesey Airlines	**Buenos Aires → Hong Kong** Jan. 31st 12:00 a.m.	27h05m	$1,000.00
	***Hong Kong → Taipei** Feb. 2nd 3:00 p.m.	18h07m	$400.00
Important: Asterisk * indicates a layover			Total: $2,955.00

BOOK THIS PRICE WITH SERENDIPITY NOW!

From:	Kamil Ahearn <kamil.acorn@thebasis.com>
To:	Serendipity Travel Agency <support@serendipityta.com>
Date:	June 17
Subject:	Change in Plans

Greetings,

I just booked a flight through your company a few minutes ago and I believe I made a bit of a mistake. I booked a return flight home to Taipei that has a connection from Hong Kong to Tokyo and the entire travel time is over forty-five hours! I don't have time for this and would really like to change flight routes if possible. I still want to keep the rest of my itinerary the same; it is only the return flights that I wish to change. If it makes things easier, I would be happy to return home on any day within a week of my original booking date.

Thanks so much and I hope to hear from you soon.

Kamil

50. In the advertisement, the "trekking" in paragraph 2, line 2, is closest in meaning to
    (A) skiing
    (B) diving
    (C) hiking
    (D) dancing

51. When is Mr. Ahearn willing to fly to Taipei?
    (A) In mid-December only
    (B) In early or late January
    (C) In late January or early February
    (D) In early February only

52. What is most likely true about the original itinerary from Hong Kong to Taipei?
    (A) It is going to be delayed.
    (B) It requires flying on two planes.
    (C) It will be cancelled by the airline.
    (D) It is fully booked.

53. What does Mr. Ahearn request from the travel agency?
    (A) He would like to change his return itinerary.
    (B) He would like to cancel his travel plans.
    (C) He would like to change the date that he leaves for vacation.
    (D) He would like a discount on his return tickets.

54. How much money should we expect Mr. Ahearn to pay in total to the travel agency to get the flights that he wants?
    (A) Exactly $400
    (B) Exactly $1,355
    (C) Exactly $2,995
    (D) over $2,995

NEW TOEIC MODEL TEST
多益全真模擬試題

🎧 *Track 99*　測驗時間：120 分鐘

Listening Test	162
Reading Test	180
TOEIC 測驗成績計算方式	210
TOEIC 模擬測驗答案紙	211

LISTENING TEST

In the Listening Test, you will be asked to demonstrate how well you understand spoken English. The entire Listening Test will last approximately 45 minutes. There are four parts, and directions are given for each part. You must mark your answers on the separate answer sheet. Do not write your answers in the test book.

PART 1

Directions: For each question in this part, you will hear four statements about a picture in your test book. When you hear the statements, you must select the one statement that best describes what you see in the picture. Then find the number of the question on your answer sheet and mark your answer. The statements will not be printed in your test book and will be spoken only one time.

Sample Answer
Ⓐ Ⓑ ● Ⓓ

Example

Statement (C), "The woman is holding a document," is the best description of the picture, so you should select answer (C) and mark it on your answer sheet.

1.

2.

3.

4.

5.

6.

PART 2

Directions: You will hear a question or statement and three responses spoken in English. They will not be printed in your test book and will be spoken only one time. Select the best response to the question or statement and mark the letter (A), (B), or (C) on your answer sheet.

Example
You will hear: What is the meeting about?
You will also hear: (A) He'll probably be late.
(B) Our new marketing plan.
(C) I have an interview.

The best response to the question "What is the meeting about?" is choice (B), "Our new marketing plan," so (B) is the correct answer. You should mark answer (B) on your answer sheet.

7. Mark your answer on your answer sheet.
8. Mark your answer on your answer sheet.
9. Mark your answer on your answer sheet.
10. Mark your answer on your answer sheet.
11. Mark your answer on your answer sheet.
12. Mark your answer on your answer sheet.
13. Mark your answer on your answer sheet.
14. Mark your answer on your answer sheet.
15. Mark your answer on your answer sheet.
16. Mark your answer on your answer sheet.
17. Mark your answer on your answer sheet.
18. Mark your answer on your answer sheet.
19. Mark your answer on your answer sheet.
20. Mark your answer on your answer sheet.
21. Mark your answer on your answer sheet.
22. Mark your answer on your answer sheet.
23. Mark your answer on your answer sheet.
24. Mark your answer on your answer sheet.
25. Mark your answer on your answer sheet.
26. Mark your answer on your answer sheet.
27. Mark your answer on your answer sheet.
28. Mark your answer on your answer sheet.
29. Mark your answer on your answer sheet.
30. Mark your answer on your answer sheet.
31. Mark your answer on your answer sheet.

PART 3

Directions: You will hear some conversations between two or more people. You will be asked to answer three questions about what the speakers say in each conversation. Select the best response to each question and mark the letter (A), (B), (C), or (D) on your answer sheet. The conversations will not be printed in your test book and will be spoken only one time.

32. What most likely is the man's occupation?
    (A) He is a food reviewer.
    (B) He is a host at a restaurant.
    (C) He is the woman's personal assistant.
    (D) He is computer repairman.

33. Which options does the man offer the woman?
    (A) She can dine at seven or nine o'clock.
    (B) She can cancel or keep her nine o'clock booking.
    (C) She can make a reservation for Friday or Saturday.
    (D) She can have a table by the door or window.

34. What does the woman plan to do?
    (A) She'll tell her friends they'll have lunch instead.
    (B) She'll tell her friends dinner is canceled.
    (C) She'll go to dinner at seven o'clock on Friday.
    (D) She'll go to dinner at nine o'clock on Friday.

Go on to the next page.

35. Where does the woman most likely work?
    (A) At an accountant's office
    (B) At a high school
    (C) At a marketing firm
    (D) At a publisher's office

36. What is the woman most likely carrying?
    (A) A small envelope
    (B) A bunch of posters
    (C) A cup of coffee
    (D) A big box

37. What might the woman not be able to do?
    (A) Finish making copies
    (B) File her client's taxes on time
    (C) Find the missing receipt
    (D) Get her tax refund this year

38. What are the speakers mainly talking about?
    (A) An upcoming staff meeting
    (B) How to send e-mails at work
    (C) How to find a new job
    (D) Why Tim might be in trouble

39. What does the woman say about the man's feelings?
    (A) He should be more worried about being fired.
    (B) He shouldn't feel responsible for what happened.
    (C) He shouldn't be pleased that Tim is in trouble.
    (D) He should act more upset when he talks to Tim.

40. What does the woman imply about the company?
    (A) Most people arrive late to work.
    (B) The staff can't send personal e-mails at work.
    (C) No one is allowed to eat at their desks.
    (D) Their boss checks everyone's e-mail account daily.

41. What is the main point of the man and woman's discussion?
    (A) Who should pay for museum tickets
    (B) If he'll go to art school
    (C) If she'll go with him to the art museum
    (D) When they should leave the museum

42. How does the woman feel about modern art?
    (A) She's not interested in it.
    (B) She's a big fan of it.
    (C) She has no opinion about it.
    (D) She doesn't know what it is.

43. How much will Jen pay to enter the museum?
    (A) She will have to pay $5.
    (B) If Sam buys a ticket, hers will be half price.
    (C) She doesn't know how much she will have to pay yet.
    (D) It doesn't cost anything to go.

44. Why does the man not want to go to the doctor?
    (A) He doesn't have time.
    (B) It might cost a lot of money.
    (C) He can't leave work to go.
    (D) He doesn't have the doctor's phone number.

45. What does the woman suggest the man do?
    (A) Go to medical school
    (B) Call the doctor's office
    (C) Wait a few more days
    (D) Go to the doctor as soon as possible

46. What can be inferred about the man?
    (A) He is a good cook.
    (B) He has medical insurance.
    (C) He doesn't have much money.
    (D) He goes to the doctor often.

Go on to the next page.

47. What does the woman want to do?
    (A) Go to a job interview at the bank
    (B) Open a new bank account
    (C) Get money from the bank
    (D) Pay her credit card bill

48. When does the woman want to make the appointment?
    (A) In the afternoon
    (B) At lunchtime
    (C) In the morning
    (D) On the weekend

49. Why can't the woman come to the bank at ten?
    (A) She needs to be at work by eleven.
    (B) She has another appointment.
    (C) Her car is not working.
    (D) She doesn't know which train to take.

---

50. What does the woman want to do?
    (A) Pick up her phone
    (B) Fix her friend's phone
    (C) Buy a used phone
    (D) Have her phone fixed

51. When did the phone's warranty end?
    (A) There never was a warranty.
    (B) It will never end.
    (C) It ended one month ago.
    (D) It will end in five days.

52. How much will the repair cost?
    (A) $25 for each day it's worked on
    (B) $25, plus the cost of parts if needed
    (C) Nothing, because the phone can't be repaired
    (D) Nothing, because it's under warranty

53. What is the man and woman's relationship?
    (A) They used to be classmates.
    (B) They used to work together.
    (C) They are business partners.
    (D) The man is the woman's boss.

54. What line of work is the man in?
    (A) He's in recruiting.
    (B) He is retired.
    (C) He's in purchasing.
    (D) He doesn't have a job.

55. What does the man say they should do?
    (A) Go to the office
    (B) Order supplies
    (C) Work together
    (D) Meet and have coffee

56. What is the conversation mainly about?
    (A) The results of an election
    (B) Product test results
    (C) A phone conference
    (D) A disagreement between two workers

57. Why does the woman say "Fahygo is a big hit"?
    (A) She thinks Fahygo is going to hurt the company.
    (B) She thinks Fahygo is going to hurt consumers.
    (C) She thinks Fahygo is going to be popular with consumers.
    (D) She thinks Fahygo is going to be too expensive.

58. What type of product is Fahygo most likely?
    (A) A food or beverage product
    (B) An entertainment device
    (C) A children's toy
    (D) An exercise machine

Go on to the next page.

59. What time of day is the conversation?
    (A) Early morning
    (B) Midafternoon
    (C) Early evening
    (D) Late at night

60. What is most likely implied when the woman says "I need a coffee for sure"?
    (A) She needs a coffee to decide.
    (B) She needs a coffee to be confident.
    (C) She absolutely needs a coffee.
    (D) She wants a coffee if possible.

61. What type of appointments are the workers going to attend?
    (A) Appointments with lawyers regarding a legal case
    (B) Appointments with realtors regarding an office space
    (C) Appointments with salespeople to discuss profits
    (D) Appointments with investors regarding a loan

62. What does the man ask a question about?
    (A) His gym membership card
    (B) His rewards at a movie theater
    (C) The location of the restrooms
    (D) The time the movie starts

63. Look at the graphic. How many points are needed to earn a free ticket?
    (A) 925
    (B) 1000
    (C) 1950
    (D) 2000

RECEIPT		
Room B	Row M	Seat 10
General Admission X 1		$9.25
Total Sale		$9.25
points earned today		18
total points balance		1950

64. Where does this conversation take place?
    (A) On a movie set
    (B) At a musical performance
    (C) At a movie theater
    (D) At a café

65. What part of the patient's health does Dr. Leary discuss?
    (A) The patient's mental state
    (B) The patient's metabolic rate
    (C) The patient's cardiovascular system
    (D) The patient's nervous system

Quarter	Blood Pressure
Q1	120/80
Q2	130/85
Q3	160/95
Q4	130/85

66. What did the man do to improve his blood pressure?
    (A) Changed his exercise routine
    (B) Changed his eating habits
    (C) Changed his profession
    (D) Changed his marital status

67. Look at the graphic. What rate does the doctor think the man can achieve in the next year?
    (A) 120/80
    (B) 130/85
    (C) 160/95
    (D) 110/70

68. What does the woman need to buy?
    (A) Science equipment
    (B) Art supplies
    (C) School books
    (D) Clothes

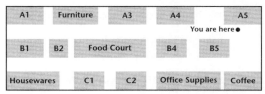

69. Which is NOT a reason the woman is going to this specific store?
    (A) She gets a discount there.
    (B) She won't need to go anywhere else.
    (C) It is the only store that sells what she needs.
    (D) The school gets a portion of the sale.

70. Look at the graphic. Where is the store most likely located?
    (A) A3
    (B) C1
    (C) B4
    (D) B2

Go on to the next page.

PART 4

Directions: You will hear some talks given by a single speaker. You will be asked to answer three questions about what the speakers say in each talk. Select the best response to each question and mark the letter (A), (B), (C), or (D) on your answer sheet. The talks will not be printed in your test book and will be spoken only one time.

71. What is the talk mainly about?
    (A) How to increase the number of customers
    (B) Why the company was started
    (C) What is happening on the factory floor
    (D) How new employees are chosen

72. What does the factory produce?
    (A) Computer cases
    (B) Cell phones
    (C) Gloves
    (D) Protective suits

73. What does the speaker say about the employees?
    (A) They work six days a week.
    (B) They aren't very busy now.
    (C) They all enjoy their jobs.
    (D) They must wear hats.

74. What is the speaker's occupation?
    (A) Airplane pilot
    (B) Flight attendant
    (C) Ground crew member
    (D) Baggage handler

75. Who is most likely being addressed?
    (A) An audience at a play
    (B) A group of airline employees
    (C) Airplane passengers
    (D) People about to board a plane

76. When will they arrive?
    (A) 7:45
    (B) 8:30
    (C) 8:45
    (D) 8:00

77. Who is the speaker probably addressing?
    (A) University professors
    (B) People who will speak at the event
    (C) Business managers
    (D) Art lovers

78. What is the speaker doing?
    (A) Asking people to donate money
    (B) Helping people find their seats
    (C) Introducing a guest speaker
    (D) Talking about a close friend

79. Who is Mark Hill?
    (A) A photographer
    (B) An abstract art expert
    (C) A museum manager
    (D) An art dealer

Go on to the next page.

80. Which problem does Kathy mention?
    (A) The wedding has run out of food.
    (B) The banquet hall the bride chose is fully booked.
    (C) The wedding date must be changed.
    (D) Most guests cannot attend the wedding.

81. Why does Kathy recommend the Ambassador Banquet Center?
    (A) There are 20 rooms available on the 5th.
    (B) It's cheaper than Morris Banquet Hall.
    (C) She's worked with that facility before.
    (D) A deposit isn't needed to book it.

82. What will Kathy do when she gets Trina's credit card number?
    (A) Pay the bill at the Morris Banquet Hall
    (B) Take back the deposit she paid for the reservation
    (C) Confirm the new banquet room reservation
    (D) Begin planning the wedding

83. How hot will it be at the beach today?
    (A) 85°
    (B) 89°
    (C) 84°
    (D) 72°

84. What is suggested that people do today?
    (A) Drink lots of water
    (B) Stay away from the beach
    (C) Wear a jacket
    (D) Leave their pets in their cars

85. How will the weather be tomorrow?
    (A) It will be the hottest day all week.
    (B) It will be very rainy.
    (C) It will be the same as today.
    (D) It will be cooler than today.

86. What does the speaker say about applying for jobs?
    (A) It's better to mail your résumé.
    (B) It's better to fax your résumé.
    (C) It's better to apply by e-mail.
    (D) It's better to apply in person.

87. What does the speaker say job applicants should do for every job?
    (A) Call the hiring manager
    (B) Just e-mail a résumé
    (C) Create a new cover letter
    (D) Get a new cell phone number

88. What is mentioned about having a cell phone?
    (A) It's good if you can be reached anytime.
    (B) It's good to check e-mail on-the-go.
    (C) It's good to play games while you're waiting.
    (D) It's good to talk to friends before an interview.

89. How often will the class meet?
    (A) Once a week
    (B) Twice a week
    (C) Twice a month
    (D) Once a month

90. What does the speaker imply when he says, "I had to learn it all from the beginning just like you"?
    (A) He attended the same school as the other students.
    (B) He used not to know how to be a teacher.
    (C) He used not to know how to run a business.
    (D) He had never used a computer before taking this class himself.

91. What will happen next?
    (A) They will study in the classroom.
    (B) They will work in the computer lab.
    (C) They will start class.
    (D) They will tour the building.

Go on to the next page.

92. What is the speaker's profession?
    (A) He is an advertiser.
    (B) He is a salesman.
    (C) He is a manager.
    (D) He is a customer service associate.

93. What does the speaker mean when he says "tune in"?
    (A) Don't be distracted by commercials.
    (B) Watch your favorite TV shows as carefully as possible.
    (C) Put on the television channel that you want to see.
    (D) Be aware of all of your options.

94. What type of business does Chillflix mainly compete with?
    (A) The medical industry
    (B) The aerospace industry
    (C) The cable industry
    (D) The finance industry

95. Why are the locations of the items being changed?
    (A) Because of the time of year
    (B) Because of poor sales
    (C) Because some items are being discontinued
    (D) Because people should eat healthier

96. Which of the following items will NOT be moved?
    (A) Candy
    (B) Breads and cakes
    (C) Home decor
    (D) Pumpkins and squash

97. Look at the graphic. From the entrance, where will the candy display be after the items are rearranged?
    (A) Next to breads and cakes
    (B) In front of the coffee and tea
    (C) Behind the discount items
    (D) Closer to the juices

Item	Amount	Unit Price
Mediabook13"	100	$999
Thinkbook13"	100	$1,149
Thinkbook15"	300	$1,999
Thinkbook17"	200	$2,499

98. Why is the man most likely speaking?
    (A) He is asking Dinesh how many items to order.
    (B) He is leaving a voicemail about a purchasing invoice.
    (C) He is asking his assistant to order more Mediabooks.
    (D) He is venting his frustration to the claims department.

99. Based on the message, how do Dinesh and Rex know each other?
    (A) They work in different departments at the same company.
    (B) Rex is Dinesh's manager.
    (C) They are both interns in the purchasing department.
    (D) They work at separate companies as buyers/sellers.

100. Look at the graphic and consider the message. How many thirteen-inch Thinkbooks did Rex order at the beginning of the month?
    (A) Zero
    (B) One Hundred
    (C) Two Hundred
    (D) Three Hundred

Go on to the next page.

READING TEST

In the Reading Test, you will read a variety of texts and answer several different types of reading comprehension questions. The entire Reading Test will last 75 minutes. There are three parts, and directions are given for each part. You are encouraged to answer as many questions as possible within the time allowed.

You must mark your answers on the separate answer sheet. Do not write your answers in the test book.

PART 5

Directions: A word or phrase is missing in each of the sentences below. Four answer choices are given below each sentence. Select the best answer to complete the sentence. Then mark the letter (A), (B), (C), or (D) on your answer sheet.

101. Clive decided to work at a company outside of the city ------- there are lots of trees and it's peaceful.
    (A) that
    (B) which
    (C) than
    (D) where

102. If the bus arrives at the station by 11:30, it will ------- us enough time to eat lunch before we check into the hotel.
    (A) given
    (B) give
    (C) giving
    (D) gave

103. The man ------- decided not to say anything after police caught him with the woman's purse.
    (A) wise
    (B) wisely
    (C) wiser
    (D) wisdom

104. My roommate has three sisters and ------- are great singers and dancers.
    (A) all of them
    (B) both of them
    (C) among them
    (D) either of them

105. The airplane ------- had to turn the plane around due to a thunderstorm that moved in suddenly.
    (A) captive
    (B) caption
    (C) captain
    (D) capital

106. Whether Tyler gets a raise or not ------- on his job performance over the next year.
    (A) depends
    (B) dependable
    (C) depend
    (D) depending

107. The actress ------- picture I have on my wall will star in a brand new play next month in New York City.
    (A) whose
    (B) whom
    (C) which
    (D) that

108. ------- we care about our employees' safety, the laboratory has a new policy about wearing safety glasses at all times.
    (A) However
    (B) While
    (C) But
    (D) Because

109. The professor ------- the students work in groups for the year-end project.
    (A) did
    (B) forced
    (C) got
    (D) had

Go on to the next page.

110. That beautiful, world-famous ------- is on exhibit at the National Art Museum right now, and I really want to see it.
    (A) appearance
    (B) painting
    (C) look
    (D) view

111. Don recommended ------- Vinny join a committee for neighborhood planning since he had complaints about the area.
    (A) when
    (B) why
    (C) where
    (D) that

112. The buses scheduled to run through the city never came on time, which caused many people to complain about the current ------- system.
    (A) education
    (B) transportation
    (C) information
    (D) pollution

113. Darla found her favorite pen in the inside pocket of her purse, right ------- her friend said it would be.
    (A) which
    (B) where
    (C) when
    (D) who

114. Shelia ordered twenty boxes of paper for the hiring department; -------, they won't arrive until later in the month.
    (A) therefore
    (B) in spite of
    (C) rather than
    (D) however

115. The more exposure the issue gets on the news, the ------- it is that people will donate money to help solve the problem.
(A) most likely
(B) likely
(C) more likely
(D) like

116. Tim can't find the Long Island Ferry schedule that he paid twelve dollars for -------.
(A) any here
(B) where
(C) nowhere
(D) anywhere

117. We should take a taxi to the airport because the buses won't be ------- that early in the morning.
(A) to run
(B) ran
(C) running
(D) runs

118. ------- the fact that there is already a large amount of garbage in the ocean, we should all work harder to recycle as much as possible.
(A) Giving
(B) Give
(C) Given
(D) Gave

119. Andrea somehow managed to win the competition ------- never participating in the sport before.
(A) despite
(B) however
(C) until
(D) nor

120. Donald runs ------- fast, so I can't keep up with him when we exercise together.
    (A) extraordinary
    (B) extremely
    (C) exactly
    (D) expressly

121. My college roommate ------- me since our freshman year by buying and wearing the same clothes that I do.
    (A) imitates
    (B) was imitating
    (C) has imitated
    (D) will imitate

122. Maggie needs to ------- down before she gets in her car because driving when one is upset is dangerous.
    (A) calm
    (B) call
    (C) clean
    (D) come

123. You are going to buy a new computer before the annual investment banking conference, -------?
    (A) won't you
    (B) aren't you
    (C) am I
    (D) aren't they

124. ------- most of the students here are studying English, Sandra has decided to learn Russian.
    (A) That
    (B) Whereas
    (C) Therefore
    (D) Such

125. Kim thinks Frank is ------- committed employee at work because he often arrives late and leaves early.
    (A) the most
    (B) the least
    (C) more than
    (D) less than

126. Bill, who was in need of a car, ------- Tammy $2,000 for one that she was selling, but she wanted more money.
    (A) offer
    (B) offered
    (C) is offering
    (D) will offer

127. If Adam had not told us, we wouldn't ------- that Tina had been promoted.
    (A) had known
    (B) be knowing
    (C) known
    (D) know

128. The *New York Times* has seen a 44 percent increase in website traffic ------- the numbers in their most recent press release are to be believed.
    (A) so that
    (B) if
    (C) though
    (D) somewhat

129. In order to increase overall customer -------, the store allowed returns and exchanges of purchases for up to 60 days.
    (A) relaxation
    (B) satisfaction
    (C) pleasure
    (D) delight

130. Tina ------- her coworker her car so he could bring his new TV home from the discount electronics store.
    (A) took
    (B) bought
    (C) borrowed
    (D) lent

Go on to the next page.

PART 6

Directions: Read the texts that follow. A word, phrase, or sentence is missing in parts of each text. Four answer choices for each question are given below the text. Select the best answer to complete the text. Then mark the letter (A), (B), (C) or (D) on your answer sheet.

Questions 131-134 refer to the following passage.

Ronald Reagan may have been the US President that loved ice cream the most. In 1984, he named July National Ice Cream Month and July 15 National Ice Cream Day. Although it may seem strange, creating a holiday to honor ice cream in America does make a lot of sense. More than ninety percent of the people living in the US enjoy eating that frozen treat. ---**131**---, Americans consume more ice cream per year than people in any other country—an average of forty-eight pints per person! And ice cream isn't just good to eat, it's also good for the ---**132**---. Since so many people love eating ice cream, the ice cream industry makes billions of dollars in sales. This means that many people have jobs making, selling, or serving that dessert. Additionally, ten percent of the milk produced in the US is purchased ---**133**--- ice cream companies, which is great for the country's farmers. Ice cream is so popular in America that it could be named the country's national dish. ---**134**---

131. (A) In that case (B) However
    (C) In fact (D) To sum up

132. (A) economy (B) economic
    (C) economics (D) economical

133. (A) from (B) by
    (C) to (D) with

134. (A) Perhaps, at least, it should be named the country's national dessert!
    (B) There are so many desserts that go well with pizza!
    (C) In summation, too much ice cream can be a dangerous thing.
    (D) After all, cookies are only second best.

Questions 135-138 refer to the following letter.

Pet Plus
125 Main Street Roseville, California 95678   Toll Free: 1-800-555-1234

Dear Valued Customer,

Thank you for joining the Pet Plus membership program! ---**135**--- Additionally, you will get special coupons that will give you huge discounts on those items.

Included in this letter is your membership card. Please bring this with you ---**136**--- you visit a Pet Plus store. Besides being able to purchase products at cheaper prices, you will also earn Pet Plus points for every ---**137**--- you spend. At the end of the year, you will be able to use these points to get amazing free gifts.

All of us at Pet Plus look forward to ---**138**--- you soon! If you have any questions about our membership program, call us at 1-800-555-1234 or visit a Pet Plus retail location to speak to a staff member.

Sincerely,

Martha Goyle
President, Pet Plus

135. (A) As a member, you will receive monthly newsletters that will be full of information about the new products we have coming to our stores.
 (B) Your application is under review, and hopefully we will have some good news for you by the end of the month.
 (C) In light of this, we are now able to process your request to return several items to our store for a full refund.
 (D) Our puppy adoption department is open every Saturday and Sunday from 6:00 a.m. to 11:30 a.m.

136. (A) whatever   (B) whenever
 (C) whoever   (D) whichever

137. (A) price   (B) cash
 (C) money   (D) dollar

138. (A) serve   (B) serving
 (C) served   (D) be serving

Go on to the next page.

Questions 139-142 refer to the following memo.

Memorandum

To: IT Department
From: Helen White, CEO
Date: August 22nd
Subject: Transfer Opportunity

I'm following ---**139**--- last week's announcement about our new branch in Austin with this memo. Now that a location has been found and an opening date has been set, we are in need of employees to staff the new branch. We would like to start the hiring process by filling the management positions and have decided to look for current employees who would be willing to transfer to the new location. If you would like to apply for the IT Manager position, you will need to have at least ten years of ---**140**--- and an excellent work record here. ---**141**--- Once these positions have been filled, we will open up general hiring for the department. Please bear in mind ---**142**--- the company will not be responsible for any moving costs if you transfer to Austin. However, you will be given two weeks of paid leave during which you can move.

---

139. (A) on
 (B) by
 (C) up
 (D) from

140. (A) experience
 (B) reference
 (C) confidence
 (D) evidence

141. (A) The positions of Web Developer, Applications Engineer, and MIS Director have already been filled.
 (B) If your records are currently located at your former place of work, please have them sent over here promptly.
 (C) For the IT Assistant Manager, five years of work history in the field is acceptable.
 (D) Those of you who choose not to move are entitled to a severance package equivalent to one month's pay for every year of service.

142. (A) if
 (B) what
 (C) when
 (D) that

Questions 143-146 refer to the following e-mail.

From:	TCooper@Showbiz.net
To:	HJaaques@Carreeon.com
Subject:	Ideas for Greg's retirement party

Dear Hattie,

As you know, our old friend from Luxten Bus Company, Greg Varnee, is up for retirement at the end of May. It's so hard to believe he has been there that long! A few of his coworkers and I have been trying to come up ---**143**--- some suitable ideas to give him an evening that he will remember, and I was hoping I could run a couple past you to see if you had any suggestions.

First, we want to have a cake made in the shape of a bus, just to remind Greg of what he will be missing. I'm sure he would understand the sentiment. I'm also hoping we can find some of the other people who used to work there ---**144**--- moved to other companies. Hopefully, some of them will have old photos we can use in a PowerPoint presentation.

So Hattie, do you have any other ideas? We still have a few months to think of something, so we don't have a ---**145**--- deadline. ---**146**---

Thanks,

Thomas Cooper

143. (A) to
 (B) on
 (C) by
 (D) with

144 (A) if
 (B) due to
 (C) since
 (D) but

145. (A) compact
 (B) remote
 (C) tight
 (D) various

146. (A) Make sure you send them over immediately so they can be approved.
 (B) If you do, feel free to send them over at your earliest convenience and I'd be happy to take a look at them.
 (C) Don't be scared to tell the truth next time.
 (D) Please submit them before the end of the month, as time is precious.

PART 7

Directions: In this part you will read a selection of texts, such as magazine and newspaper articles, e-mails, and instant messages. Each text or set of texts is followed by several questions. Select the best answer for each question and mark the letter (A), (B), (C), or (D) on your answer sheet.

Questions 147-148 refer to the following exchange of text message chain.

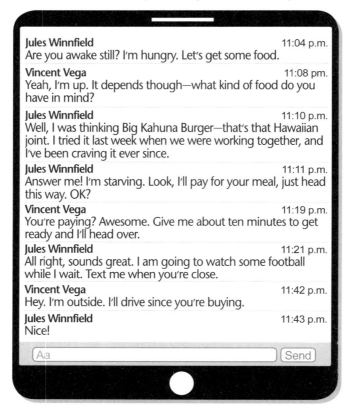

147. What is the main focus of this text conversation?
    (A) Two men deciding what to watch on TV
    (B) Two men deciding to get a late-night meal together
    (C) Two men planning a business meeting
    (D) Two men trying to decide who will drive to buy food

148. At 11:11, what does Mr. Winnfield most likely mean when he writes, "head this way"?
    (A) He wants Mr. Vega to come to where he is located.
    (B) He wants Mr. Vega to look at him.
    (C) He is explaining to Mr. Vega how to get to his house.
    (D) He is telling Mr. Vega to be careful on his way.

Questions 149-150 refer to the following advertisement.

Paradise Vacations

Don't leave your holiday up to chance! Let Paradise Vacations help you book the perfect once-in-a-lifetime trip in a beautiful tropical country. Perhaps you'd enjoy an active holiday surfing and scuba diving off the coast of Australia, or maybe a laid-back week tanning on a beach in Bali would be more your style. No matter what you like doing, the knowledgeable staff at Paradise Vacations can help you create a vacation package that will satisfy your needs.

Holiday services that we can reserve for you:

- Flights
- Hotel rooms
- Meals at restaurants
- Water sport lessons
- Sightseeing tours
- Spa packages

No other company does as much for their customers as Paradise Vacations. If you'd like to make your next vacation the perfect trip, contact us now!

345 Wellington Dr.
(800) 455-3384
E-mail: custservice@paradisevacations.net

- **Monday – Friday:** 10 a.m. to 6:30 p.m.
- **Saturday & Sunday:** 11 a.m. to 8:00 p.m.

149. What is Paradise Vacations?
    (A) It's a resort on a tropical island.
    (B) It's a surfing school in Australia.
    (C) It's an airline.
    (D) It's a travel agency.

150. What is NOT mentioned in the ad for Paradise Vacations?
    (A) Where the company is located
    (B) What they can book for clients
    (C) How much they charge customers
    (D) When they are open on weekends

Go on to the next page.

Questions 151-152 refer to the following cover letter.

Reggie Black

1540 Riverside Ave.
Columbus, OH 43085
740-558-4822
rblack@trustmail.com

Dear Sir or Madam,

My name is Reggie Black, and I am interested in applying for the position I saw posted on your company's website. My résumé is attached to this e-mail, along with two letters of reference from previous employers.

I hope that upon reading my résumé, you will be interested in granting me an interview. I have more than a decade of experience in sales, which is more than your advertisement said was needed to be considered for the position. Additionally, I've attended several training programs in the past that focused on improving one's sales abilities. I believe that if you decide to meet with me, you will find that I could be a perfect fit for the position you need filled.

If you have any questions, please call the number listed on my résumé at any time. Thank you for taking the time to read this and my supporting documents.

Sincerely,

Reggie Black

---

151. What did Reggie include with his e-mail?
    (A) A copy of his diploma
    (B) Messages from people he used to work for
    (C) Proof that he completed a training program
    (D) Reports on his behavior from former customers

152. Why does Reggie think he is a good candidate for the position?
    (A) He is very eager to move into a new industry.
    (B) He has done similar work for more than ten years.
    (C) He has completed a distinguished degree program.
    (D) He is available to begin working right away.

Questions 153-155 refer to the following meeting agenda.

Design Committee Meeting

Date/Time: January 15th, 9 a.m. to 11 a.m.
Location: Conference Room F
Attendees: Nancy Green, Barry Williams, Kurt Hamilton, Kim Bass, Ryan Holden

OBJECTIVE

In this month's meeting, we will make a final decision on the packaging design for the new line of products being released in the fourth quarter this year. Every committee member will receive information about all of the possibilities prior to the meeting and should be prepared to discuss them and offer suggestions about how to improve them. Then we will vote on which one to actually produce.

SCHEDULE
9:00 to 9:15: Call to Order by Chairperson
9:15 to 9:30: Review Previous Meeting's Minutes
9:30 to 10:30: Discuss Packaging Designs
10:30 to 10:45: Vote on Packaging Choices
10:45 to 11:00: Wrap-up and Final Questions

ROLES/RESPONSIBILITIES
Chairperson: Nancy Green
Secretary: Kurt Hamilton

---

153. What is the main purpose of the upcoming meeting?
    (A) To submit artwork that can be used on new packaging
    (B) To talk about the meeting held in the previous month
    (C) To choose a packaging design for a new product line
    (D) To assign responsibilities for a product launch event

154. The word "produce" in the objective section, line 5, is closest in meaning to:
    (A) show
    (B) make
    (C) cause
    (D) present

155. When will the committee members make a decision on the packaging?
    (A) During a discussion from 9:30 to 10:30
    (B) At the beginning of the meeting
    (C) After they leave the meeting
    (D) Between 10:30 and 10:45

Go on to the next page.

Questions 156-158 refer to the following recipe.

Baked Dijon Salmon

Directions:
1. Preheat oven to 400 degrees F.
2. Place a small pot on a stove burner and melt ¼ cup butter.
3. Stir together the melted butter, 3 tablespoons Dijon mustard, and 1 ½ tablespoons honey in a small bowl. Set aside.
4. In another bowl, mix together ¼ cup bread crumbs, ¼ cup finely chopped pecans, and 4 teaspoons chopped fresh parsley.
5. Place four salmon fillets in a baking dish.
6. With a brush, cover each salmon fillet lightly with the honey mustard mixture, and then sprinkle the tops of the fillets with the bread crumb mixture.
7. Bake the salmon for 12 to 15 minutes in the oven.
8. Remove from the oven and let cool. Place a slice of lemon on each fillet. Serve.

Makes four servings.

156. How much honey is needed to prepare this dish?
    (A) None
    (B) ¼ cup
    (C) 1 ½ teaspoons
    (D) 1 ½ tablespoons

157. Which of the following actions should be performed first?
    (A) Four salmon fillets should be placed in a pan.
    (B) Mustard should be poured in a bowl.
    (C) The oven should be turned on.
    (D) Butter should be melted on the stove.

158. What is TRUE about this recipe?
    (A) The salmon is cooked in a saucepan.
    (B) It is supposed to feed four people.
    (C) Four cups of bread crumbs are needed for it.
    (D) The butter is mixed with the bread crumbs in a bowl.

Questions 159-161 refer to the following e-mail.

To:	customerservice@lilysdiner.com
From:	soccermom@mailbox.com
Subject:	Complaint

To Whom It May Concern:

Last Wednesday night, I came into your restaurant to eat with my family, and I was very disappointed with our experience. First of all, when we arrived, there was no one at the entrance to greet us. It took almost 15 minutes for someone to notice us and take us to a table. Second, our waitress, Mandy, was terribly rude. She wouldn't look at us when we were talking to her, and when she came out with our drinks, she slammed them down on the table so hard that one tipped over and spilled all over my daughter. And she didn't even apologize! At that point, I was so angry that we got up to leave, and you know what happened? The final problem of the evening was the reaction of the manager. He made us pay for the drinks we ordered even though we didn't touch them! I will never visit Lily's Diner again!

Sincerely,

Joanne Parker

159. Why was this letter written?
    (A) Joanne wanted to compliment Mandy on her service.
    (B) Joanne wanted to complain about a recent experience.
    (C) Joanne wanted to make a dinner reservation.
    (D) Joanne wanted to ask questions about a problem.

160. Why did Joanne wait so long for a table?
    (A) The restaurant was very busy.
    (B) Her table was still being cleaned.
    (C) No one saw her enter the restaurant.
    (D) The restaurant wasn't open when she came.

161. What happened to Joanne's daughter?
    (A) She wasn't allowed to enter the restaurant.
    (B) She was served her meal before everyone else.
    (C) She fought with the manager.
    (D) She got covered in a liquid.

Questions 162-164 *refer to the following schedule.*

Martin and Lee's Weekly Schedule for April 17th – April 23rd

	Monday	Tuesday	Wednesday	Thursday	Friday
9-10 am	*Lee:* Breakfast meeting with new client	*Lee:* Drop off car at mechanic on way to work	*Martin:* Job interview	*Lee:* Tennis with client	*Lee:* Leave for business trip (2 weeks)
10-11 am					
11-12 pm				*Martin:* Soccer practice	
12-1 pm		*Lee:* Lunch with brother and sister			*Martin:* Lunch with Betty
1-2 pm	*Martin:* Finance class final				
2-3 pm			*Lee:* Pick up car		
3-4 pm		*Martin:* English class final			
4-5 pm					
5-6 pm					
6-7 pm	*Martin:* Watch hockey game	*Martin and Lee:* Chores		*Lee:* Movie with Tina	
7-8 pm			*Martin:* Dinner with Mom		
8-9 pm					

162. When will Martin and Lee probably do their laundry?
    (A) Tuesday at 6 p.m.
    (B) Wednesday at 10 a.m.
    (C) Thursday at 11 a.m.
    (D) Friday at 9 a.m.

163. What will Martin be doing on Wednesday morning?
    (A) He'll be finishing up a final at school.
    (B) He'll be trying to get a position at a company.
    (C) He'll be picking up the car after it's repaired.
    (D) He'll be doing something athletic with friends.

164. What is most likely Martin and Lee's relationship?
    (A) Brothers   (B) Roommates
    (C) Coworkers   (D) Classmates

Questions 165-168 refer to the following memo.

Attention, Third Floor Employees:

—[1]— Starting on October 16th, the third floor of this building will be undergoing maintenance work that will last for two months. —[2]— Please note that there will be several days when employees have no access to their work stations on the third floor because of safety issues. Those dates are listed below, and everyone will receive e-mail reminders two days prior to them. On those dates, employees normally working on the third floor will be temporarily assigned to the fourth or sixth floor. —[3]— We apologize for the inconvenience and thank you for your patience while we make improvements to the facilities. —[4]—

The third floor will be closed to all employees on:
- October 22nd & 23rd
- November 1st – 6th
- November 14th
- December 1st – 3rd

165. How will employees be reminded about closures of the third floor?
 (A) There will be more announcements posted on the fourth and sixth floors.
 (B) They will be sent e-mails two days before the floor is closed.
 (C) They will receive e-mails on the days that they must go to another floor.
 (D) The supervisors they report to will put written reminders in their mailboxes.

166. Where will employees go when the third floor is closed?
 (A) They will work from home and communicate through e-mail.
 (B) They won't be required to work on those days.
 (C) They will all be assigned new offices on the fourth floor.
 (D) They will either work on the fourth floor or sixth floor.

167. In which of the following positions marked [1], [2], [3], and [4] does the following sentence best belong?
 "Employees will receive e-mails detailing exactly where to go and who to report to during that time."
 (A) [1]   (B) [2]
 (C) [3]   (D) [4]

168. On which of the following dates will the third floor be closed?
 (A) October 16th   (B) October 24th
 (C) November 15th   (D) December 2nd

Questions 169-172 refer to the following notice.

Due to a shortage in bookings this weekend, the Hilliard Hotel and Spa is offering huge discounts to local residents who come visit us today or tomorrow.

—[1]— For just $50, you can sleep in one of our world-class suites and receive a complimentary in-room massage. Guests other than yourself are welcome to stay in the same room, but a small $5 fee will be added to your bill for each one aged 18 or over. To take advantage of this special deal, you just need to show an ID that proves you live in Hilliard. —[2]— Come in and order an appetizer and entrée, and you'll get 30% off your bill.

—[3]— Hilliard Hotel and Spa has been operating in Hilliard for more than twenty years, and this is the first time that it has offered such amazing deals specifically for the local community. —[4]— If you haven't come to check us out yet, now is the perfect time to do so. We look forward to seeing you soon!

169. Who would be most interested in this notice?
    (A) A traveler who just arrived in the area
    (B) A local resident
    (C) Someone planning a vacation abroad
    (D) A family going on a trip in a few weeks

170. How much would a family of four pay for a room if the two children were 15 and 18?
    (A) $50
    (B) $55
    (C) $60
    (D) $65

171. What does a person need to do in order to receive a discount on a meal?
    (A) If a person buys an entrée, he or she will get an appetizer for free.
    (B) A diner must order two items off the menu to get the discount.
    (C) Anyone who books a room at the hotel will get 30% off a meal.
    (D) A person just needs to prove residence in Hilliard to get a cheaper dish.

172. In which of the following positions marked [1], [2], [3], and [4] does the following sentence best belong?
    "Besides huge discounts on rooms, we are also greatly reducing the prices of meals in our dining room."
    (A) [1]
    (B) [2]
    (C) [3]
    (D) [4]

Questions 173-175 refer to the following online chat discussion.

Mike Bello [22:11]:
You guys, this year-end expense report stuff is killing me.

Sarah Lin [22:13]:
Tell me about it! I'm on the hunt for two or three receipts from business lunches last month that it seems have disappeared.

Ian O'Brien [22:15]:
Oh, big deal! I've got stacks of credit card bills and things I don't even remember buying . . .

Sarah Lin [22:16]:
Well, excuse me, sir . . . Just kidding. Need some help?

Ian O'Brien [22:18]:
I might actually, but not with this. Are you almost done?

Sarah Lin [22:21]:
Hardly. It's just . . . this paperwork is so unclear! What about Mike?

Mike Bello [22:25]:
Yeah, I might be able to help. What's up, Ian?

Ian O'Brien [22:29]:
Well, besides all this year-end expense reporting business, I should be working on the proposal for the company's new hiring procedures. We have to meet our new recruiting goals for next quarter.

Mike Bello [22:36]:
Yuck. What can I help with there?

Ian O'Brien [22:39]:
I just need to give it a second set of eyes—make sure it makes sense.

173. In which department does Ian O'Brien most likely work?
    (A) Finance
    (B) Marketing
    (C) HR
    (D) Sales

174. Why is Sarah Lin taking a long time completing her expense report?
    (A) She has too many items.
    (B) She doesn't understand how to fill out the forms.
    (C) She doesn't have the applications she needs.
    (D) She can't remember the necessary dates.

175. At 22:15, what does Ian O'Brien imply when he writes, "big deal"?
    (A) Sarah's report is very challenging.
    (B) He's glad he doesn't have as much work as her.
    (C) Sarah shouldn't complain about what she needs to do.
    (D) He's glad he is almost done.

Go on to the next page.

Questions 176-180 refer to the following e-mail and response.

To:	jenna_bog@email.com
From:	hr@lavaindustries.com
Subject:	Position in Accounting

Dear Ms. Bog,

First, I'd like to thank you for your interest in the junior accountant position at Lava Industries. We have looked over the résumé you e-mailed to us and feel that you have a lot of the qualities we are looking for. For that reason, we would like to offer you a chance to interview for the position. This first round of interviews will be a panel interview, and the panel will be made up of a representative from HR, one from accounting, and one from management. If you successfully complete the first interview, you will be invited back for a second one, which will be one-on-one.

Please note that if the first interview goes well, we will also then contact two references and ask them about your past work experience and your abilities. Their recommendations will also help determine if you will be right for the job. When you come to the first interview, please bring phone numbers for the two people you would like us to call.

If you would like to accept this interview offer, please reply directly to this e-mail and indicate whether you would like to come in on Wednesday at 11 a.m., Thursday at 3 p.m., or Friday at 8:30 a.m. Thank you and have a nice day.

Sincerely,

Martha Hendricks
HR Manager, Lava Industries

To:	hr@lavaindustries.com
From:	jenna_bog@email.com
Subject:	RE: Position in Accounting

Dear Ms. Hendricks,

Thank you very much for inviting me for an interview. I am so excited about being considered for the position of junior accountant at Lava Industries.

I would like to accept your offer for an interview and would like to reserve the Wednesday time slot. I will bring along the information you requested.

I look forward to meeting you soon.

Sincerely,

Jenna Bog

176. How did Jenna apply for a position at Lava Industries?
    (A) She filled out an online application.
    (B) She sent her résumé to the HR department.
    (C) She handed her résumé to someone at a hiring event.
    (D) She asked her friend Martha to recommend her.

177. Who will Jenna have her first interview with at Lava Industries?
    (A) Jenna will just meet with Martha Hendricks for her first interview.
    (B) Jenna will have a one-on-one interview with a representative from the company.
    (C) Jenna will meet with three people who are from different departments.
    (D) Jenna will have a group interview with several accountants at the company.

178. What will happen if Jenna passes her first interview?
    (A) Someone from Lava Industries will get in touch with two people she knows.
    (B) She will be offered the junior accountant position that she applied for.
    (C) It will immediately be followed by several one-on-one interviews.
    (D) She must have two people call Martha Hendricks before her second interview.

179. When will Jenna have her panel interview?
    (A) After she completes the one-on-one interview
    (B) On Friday at 8:30 a.m.
    (C) On Wednesday at 11 a.m.
    (D) After she submits two references

180. What will Jenna bring with her to her first interview?
    (A) The e-mail address of her most recent supervisor
    (B) The phone numbers of two people who know her
    (C) Another copy of her résumé
    (D) Her current contact information

Go on to the next page.

Questions 181-185 refer to the following letter to an advice columnist and the reply.

Dear Problem Coach,

I'm having some trouble, and I was hoping that you could give me some good advice. You see, after graduating from college, I decided to move across the country to start a new life on my own. At first, I lived in a large apartment with a roommate, but that didn't work out so well. That person rarely paid his part of the rent on time, and he never gave me money for his share of the bills, so I had to kick him out. And when he left, he stole my TV and my computer! From then on, I thought it was best to live on my own, so I moved to a smaller place. However, even that is too expensive, and after paying so much in rent every month, I don't have any money left to save. I would say that my rent takes up about 50% of my monthly salary.

I'm worried that I will never be able to buy my own home or even retire someday because it's impossible for me to save any money. Please help me! What should I do?

William

Dear William,

It sounds like you are having a tough time right now. Just remember, the period right after college is the hardest for everyone financially. It is especially hard nowadays because the competition for jobs is greater than it ever was before. However, if you are really spending 50% of your monthly income on your rent, you definitely need to make a change. Your first option would be to look for a higher paying job. Your rent should equal 20% to 25% of your salary, so you will need a job that pays enough to make that possible. Your second option would be to move. Either find an even cheaper place to live on your own, or move into a new place with a roommate. Of course, try to find a more honest person to live with this time. And now your last option: move back home. If your parents would be willing to let you live with them for free, it would give you time to save a lot of money. And who knows? You might end up with enough savings for a down payment on your own home.

Good luck to you!

Problem Coach

181. Why is William looking for advice?
    (A) He's not sure if he should use his savings to buy a home.
    (B) He recently lost his job and doesn't know what to do next.
    (C) He wants a new roommate, but he needs help finding a good one.
    (D) He needs help finding a way to increase his savings.

182. Which of the following did William's roommate do?
    (A) He paid his bills late every month.
    (B) He didn't give William any rent money.
    (C) He took some of William's things.
    (D) He moved without telling William.

183. What does Problem Coach say about the current job market?
    (A) The job market is more competitive today than in the past.
    (B) Only businesses in certain industries are hiring.
    (C) To find a good job, one might have to move to another city.
    (D) Most people aren't paid as much as they should be.

184. Based on Problem Coach's advice, if William's rent is $1,000 a month, which monthly salary should he try to earn?
    (A) Under $1,000
    (B) $2,000 to $3,000
    (C) $4,000 to $5,000
    (D) The same salary he has now.

185. Why does Problem Coach think William should live with his parents?
    (A) His parents probably miss having him in their home.
    (B) It could give him the chance to save a lot of money.
    (C) He would be able to buy their home when they get older.
    (D) It's nicer living with one's parents than with a roommate.

Questions 186-190 refer to the following purchase order, e-mail, and response.

Baking Supplies World		Purchase Order	
		Date	October 11th
Bill To:	Ellie's Bakery 3322 Elmwood Ave. Baltimore, M.D. 21205	Reference Number	11371
		Ship Via:	Ground
		Billing Term:	3 Months
Item Number	Item Description	Quantity	Unit Price	Total
6023	Baking Tray	4	$15.00	$60.00
8821	White Apron	2	$4.00	$8.00
7886	Metal Mixing Bowl	3	$21.00	$63.00
			Subtotal	$131.00
			Tax	-
			Shipping	$12.00
			Total	$143.00

To:	ellie@elliesbakery.com
From:	megan@bakingsuppliesworld.com
Subject:	Your Recent PO

Dear Ellie,

Thank you for your recent order with Baking Supplies World. We are happy to do business with you again. There are a few things I want to tell you before we send out your order, though. First, you may have noticed that your billing term has changed. This is because you have successfully completed an order with us in the past. Now you have the option to make payments over three months rather than pay your balance in full when your shipment arrives. Second, are you aware you could upgrade to air shipping for just $5 more than ground? If you would like to change your shipping method, please contact us before 6 p.m. on Friday. Finally, I would just like to make it clear that you are not being charged tax on this order because you moved your store to a different state. Only Virginia-based companies are subject to tax. If you have any further questions, please don't hesitate to contact us.

Sincerely,

Megan Health
Baking Supplies World, Customer Service Representative

To:	megan@bakingsuppliesworld.com
From:	ellie@elliesbakery.com
Subject:	Re: Your Recent PO

Thank you so much! You guys have great customer service and the best materials for baking. I am going to pay my balance in full just because I'm no good at accounting, so that will be easier for me. Air shipping is great for me because I need those supplies ASAP.

Thanks again. You made me glad I moved to Maryland.

Ellie of Ellie's Bakery

186. How much will Ellie pay for all the bowls she ordered?
    (A) $4.00
    (B) $21.00
    (C) $63.00
    (D) $143.00

187. What is TRUE about Ellie's purchase order?
    (A) She submitted it three months before she needed the items.
    (B) She doesn't have to pay anything to have her items shipped.
    (C) She has four different items listed on the order.
    (D) She is ordering more baking trays than metal bowls.

188. Why was Ellie's billing term changed?
    (A) Ellie has placed and paid for an order with Baking Supplies World before.
    (B) Ellie requested that she be given more time to pay off her balance.
    (C) Any order sent to another state can be paid for over several months.
    (D) Baking Supplies World now offers a three-month billing term to all customers.

189. How is this order NOT different from Ellie's previous order?
    (A) She is going to have to items shipped by air.
    (B) She is going to pay for the items in one lump sum.
    (C) She is going to have the items shipped to Maryland.
    (D) She is not going to pay tax on the items.

190. What is the main purpose of Megan's letter?
    (A) She wants to explain why she can't fill Ellie's order.
    (B) She wants to confirm that Ellie's Bakery sells the items she needs.
    (C) She wants to give Ellie information related to her order.
    (D) She wants to inform Ellie about why the cost of shipping has increased.

Questions 191-195 refer to the following chart, e-mail, and response.

Advertising Budget Third Quarter

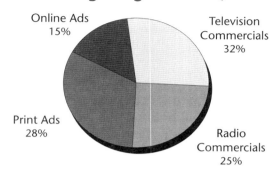

- We don't plan to run many television commercials, but the ones we do want to run are during expensive time slots.
- Print ads historically are effective during this time of year. They shouldn't remain so high in the following quarter.
- We will be able to run a very high number of radio commercials with this budget.
- We should consider assigning staff members who strictly work on online ads.

To: everett@xyzcompany.com
From: colin@xyzcompany.com
Subject: Advertising Budget

Everett,

I've just received the advertising budget you are proposing for the third quarter, and I have a few questions. First of all, why are radio commercials getting such a high percentage of the budget? I thought that they were only given 15% of last quarter's budget, and in the quarterly meeting we agreed that even that was too much. I mean, are people even listening to the radio anymore? I feel like spending money on radio ads is like throwing money away.

Next, why aren't we dedicating more money to online advertising? In my opinion, Internet ads are great because they're seen by so many people and don't cost as much as traditional media ads. My suggestion is that we cut the radio ads to 5% of the budget and put that extra 20% towards online ads. In fact, I think we should also decrease the print ad budget and pour more into online ads. How about we give print ads just 15% of the budget? That should be enough for a flyer and an ad in the local newspaper, right?

Get back to me as soon as possible with your thoughts. The new budget has to be approved by Friday.

Colin

To:	colin@xyzcompany.com
From:	everett@xyzcompany.com
Subject:	Re: Advertising Budget

Colin,

We're in agreement about the radio ads. The thing is that I mentioned the idea of cutting radio's budget to the boss, and he said he would not approve such a proposal. My hands are tied. That said, radio ads are ridiculously cheap now, so we might get decent returns.

I'll tell you what I'm thinking though. In the upcoming quarter, we use some of the online-ads budget to do research on which area of market is getting the best ROI. That should prove us right and allow us to create a budget in line with your suggestions in the fourth quarter.

Everett

191. Why is Colin writing to Everett?
    (A) He thinks Everett is spending too much money on advertising.
    (B) He doesn't believe Everett divided the advertising budget up well.
    (C) He wants to help Everett create a new advertisement for the company.
    (D) He needs help understanding the new radio commercial Everett made.

192. What is the main problem Colin has with Everett's budget proposal?
    (A) He thinks too much will be wasted on worthless types of ads.
    (B) He doesn't think Everett should change the budget from last quarter.
    (C) He would prefer to spend less money on television commercials.
    (D) He isn't sure if Everett will be able to complete it on time.

193. Which percentage of the budget would Colin like to dedicate to online ads?
    (A) 15%   (B) 35%
    (C) 48%   (D) 52%

194. Which area of the budget do Everett and Colin both agree on?
    (A) Most of the advertisements they create should be posted online.
    (B) The amount of money spent on radio ads should be cut.
    (C) The ad budget spent on TV commercials should be increased.
    (D) Flyers and newspaper ads are the most effective print advertisements.

195. Why doesn't Everett propose to decrease the budget for radio ads?
    (A) Radio ads cost a lot of money at this time of year.
    (B) Everett believes radio ads should never be decreased.
    (C) Everett wants to make sure every radio listener hears their ads.
    (D) The boss told him not to lower the budget for radio.

Go on to the next page.

Questions 196-200 rerefer to the following order confirmation, invoice, and e-mail.

From:	Shantrice Wellmore <sweetwater.boats@xumail.com>
To:	Lester Claypool <tommythecat@bestmail.com>
Date:	August 1
Subject:	Order #4565

Hello!

I hope this e-mail finds you well, Mr. Claypool. I am writing to confirm that your full payment has been received for your brand-new Endeavor V506—congratulations. Our next step in the process is to have the vehicle delivered to your house. Since you are located in Miami, Florida, we will be working with our Southeastern towing company, Mr. Schwifty Wheels, to ensure the delivery of your watercraft on time. We guarantee the shipment will arrive during the last week of August, as long as no changes are made to the order. (Changes requested within five days of this order confirmation are afforded the same guarantee.)

Attached is a copy of the invoice with all of the specifications you have selected for your vehicle. If there are any discrepancies, please contact me as soon as possible, as the technicians will be wrapping up your order over the next few days.

Thank you so much and I look forward to hearing from you!

Shantrice Wellmore
Sales Representative
Sweetwater Watercraft
1.450.226.5897
Monterey, CA 93940

Endeavor V506　　　　　　　　　　**Order #: 4565**
Comfort & Interior　　　　　　　　**Purchasing Invoice**

- Solid khaya floor
- Jet-black leather interior
- Fiberglass interior headliner
- Convertible V-berth lounge with drawer
- Starboard-side hanging locker, cedar lined
- 3-switch panel with 8 overhead LED lights and 4 accent lights
- Boze audio stereo with Bluetooth streaming, Boze audio speakers, subwoofer, and Boze audio amplifier
- 42" flat-screen TV
- 11-gallon 220v stainless steel water heater

From:	Lester Claypool <tommythecat@bestmail.com>
To:	Shantrice Wellmore <sweetwater.boats@xmail.com>
Date:	August 2
Subject:	ORDER ERROR – Order #4565

Shantrice,

Good afternoon. Hey, there is a huge problem with my order. Based off of the information you provided me, there are two errors regarding the interior design and upholstery. First, I ordered champagne leather interior, not black. Second, the TV screen you have listed is ten inches too small. I ordered the largest size possible as I plan on hosting lots of parties for sporting events.
I hope it's not too late to make sure these changes are taken care of. I look forward to your response e-mail. I appreciate your shipment policy, but I'd like to ask you to delay shipment by one week. I have work off that entire week, so it'll be more convenient for me then.

Thanks again,

Les

196. In the order confirmation, the phrase "wrapping up" in paragraph 2, line 3, is closest in meaning to
    (A) finalizing
    (B) packaging
    (C) summarizing
    (D) redoing

197. What is an Endeavor V506?
    (A) A plane
    (B) A train
    (C) An automobile
    (D) A boat

198. Which of the following is NOT a feature of the order?
    (A) A water heater
    (B) LED lights
    (C) Seat warmers
    (D) A speaker system

199. What is true about the TV?
    (A) The TV is available in various colors.
    (B) The TV is separate from the vehicle.
    (C) Mr. Claypool originally ordered a 52" TV.
    (D) Mr. Claypool ordered the wrong TV.

200. When will the Endeavor V506 arrive at Mr. Claypool's address?
    (A) In mid-August
    (B) During the last week of August
    (C) During the first week of September
    (D) At the end of September

TOEIC 測驗成績計算方式

分別計算「聽力單元」與「閱讀單元」答對的題數，各單元答對的題數就是該單元的原始分數。將你的聽力及閱讀原始分數分別登記在以下欄位中，然後將你的原始分數範圍對照下表的評量分數範圍，並各自登記在聽力與閱讀單元的評量分數範圍欄位中。兩者相加即為多益總分範圍。

	原始分數	評量分數範圍
聽力單元		
閱讀單元		
總分範圍		

TOEIC 測驗分數換算對照表

聽力單元		閱讀單元	
原始分數範圍	評量分數範圍	原始分數範圍	評量分數範圍
96–100	485–495	96–100	455–495
91–95	465–495	91–95	430–475
86–90	450–490	86–90	410–450
81–85	425–470	81–85	385–430
76–80	400–450	76–80	355–405
71–75	385–420	71–75	330–375
66–70	350–400	66–70	295–350
61–65	330–375	61–65	265–315
56–60	305–350	56–60	240–285
51–55	270–325	51–55	210–260
46–50	240–290	46–50	180–230
41–45	210–260	41–45	150–200
36–40	170–225	36–40	120–170
31–35	135–190	31–35	95–140
26–30	105–155	26–30	70–115
21–25	80–125	21–25	50–90
16–20	55–100	16–20	35–70
11–15	30–75	11–15	15–55
6–10	10–50	6–10	10–40
1–5	5–30	1–5	5–20
0	5	0	5

學英語 沒有不勞而獲的
訂本互動英語雜誌吧

☑ 訂閱滿3個月，可隨時更換
LiveABC互動英語 雜誌家族其他雜誌，
不限次數！滿足不同階段的學習需求。

初級
ABC互動英語
圖解動畫
文法句型
E-mail寫作
適用全民英檢初級、國中基測

中級
Live互動英語
生活圖解
流行實用
旅遊文化
適用全民英檢中級、大學
學測&指考、一般成人會話

中高級
ALL+互動英語
進階閱讀
寫作訓練
經典文學
適用全民英檢中高級、大學
學測&指考、一般成人會話

職場
biz互動英語
商業會話
開會簡報
商業趨勢
適用上班族、社會新鮮人

新聞
CNN互動英語
CNN官方授權
最多教師推薦
適用準備出國或生活中需要
大量使用英語溝通者

網路訂購專區
http://www.liveabc.com
雜誌館搶訂

電話專人訂購
(02)2578-2626 # 229、288
週一至週五9:00~6:00PM

光碟黏貼處